Dancing with the Moon

MY SPIRITUAL JOURNEY THROUGH IVF

Emma Després

I AM SELF-
PUBLISHING

@iamselfpub
www.iamselfpublishing.com

Contents

The Owl and the Pussycat

By Edward Lear

The Owl and the Pussycat went to sea
In a beautiful pea-green boat,
They took some honey, and plenty of money,
Wrapped up in a five-pound note.
The Owl looked up to the stars above,
And sang to a small guitar,
"O lovely Pussy! O Pussy, my love,
What a beautiful Pussy you are,
   You are,
   You are!
What a beautiful Pussy you are!"

Pussy said to the Owl, "You elegant fowl!
How charmingly sweet you sing!
O let us be married! Too long we have tarried:
But what shall we do for a ring?"
They sailed away, for a year and a day,
To the land where the Bong-Tree grows
And there in a wood, a Piggy-wig stood
With a ring at the end of his nose,
   His nose,
   His nose,
With a ring at the end of his nose.

"Dear Pig, are you willing to sell for one shilling
Your ring?" Said the Piggy, "I will."
So they took it away, and were married next day
By the Turkey who lives on the hill.
They dined on mince, and slices of quince,
Which they ate with a runcible spoon;
And hand in hand, on the edge of the sand,
They danced by the light of the moon,
   The moon,
   The moon,
They danced by the light of the moon.

About the Author

Emma is passionate about many things, but especially family, yoga, Reiki, Guernsey, Nepal, the moon, sea swimming, soaking in the bath while reading a good book, women's health and wellbeing (especially fertility), realising our potential, and living a life of purpose. Based in beautiful Guernsey, Emma teaches a regular schedule of yoga classes, as well as running yoga & wellbeing retreats on Herm Island and in Glastonbury, UK and Goa, India, and offers Level One and Level Two Reiki attunement sessions.

On Emma's website at www.beinspiredby.co.uk, you will find a number of free yoga videos, meditation and relaxation audios, and a self-help page, designed to help you to help yourself. On this page, you will find a section (amongst others) dedicated to fertility issues with links to the relevant free yoga video and audio practices that Emma recommends, together with details of her other tips.

To my three boys, without whom
none of this would have been possible.
You are my everything. x

The Words You Never Want to Hear

It was one of those moments that will be forever etched in my mind; one of those moments when time stands still and life suspends.

Here we were, E and I, being told by the specialist, Mr Nzewi, that we may not be able to have children of our own.

Not have children of our own.

Not have my own children.

The words went around in my head as I tried to process them.

I had yearned to have my own children for as long as I could remember. It was a lifelong dream. And now, here I was, sitting in the specialist's office in Guernsey, being told that my dream might never become a reality. No part of this dream had come easily to me, so perhaps I shouldn't have been surprised. I knew something wasn't right, but hearing those words, well… they're not really words that you want to hear.

Needless to say, the rest of the appointment drifted over me. There was talk of donors, adoption and of more tests, so there was still some hope. The specialist was relatively upbeat and joked about the advert from one of the main supermarket chains in the UK, saying that we too should embrace the concept of "every little helps", as he patted his bum, as they do in the advert. I'll never forget that, not least because he was trying to be positive, but because it's true, and it has stuck in my mind ever since.

The moment I reached the car, I burst into tears. It wasn't so much that I was thinking, at that moment, that we really wouldn't have children of our own; it was just the reality that it was not going to be like I had imagined. I'm a spiritual person, and I had in my mind the conscious spiritual conception with rose petals and gentle music – well, OK, perhaps not the rose petals, but you know what I mean! Besides, I'd been preparing my body for months and months, and yet that was not enough.

It was ironic really, because in actual fact, it hadn't just taken months and months; it had taken years and years. That's years and years of me searching the world to find the man with whom I may want to have children, only to find him right under my nose here in Guernsey, and a few more up and down years with him to get to a point where we both accepted we were ready to settle down and commit, and another year before he finally agreed to the idea of having a child. And now, here we were, a further year down the line, being told that we might not be able to have one after all…

PART 1

The Battle to Get Pregnant

Chapter 1

The Very Beginning

We had been trying to conceive for a year, because that is the time period you are encouraged to try before you seek medical advice, but it felt like an awfully long time, and I was desperate for some help.

Initially, I really hadn't thought we would have any trouble, as we were both very healthy. I was 36 years old at the time, a yoga teacher and Reiki Master. I was practicing yoga daily, and exercising regularly, not only swimming at a health club a few times a week, but playing competitive netball weekly. I was also receiving regular holistic treatments, a combination of Reiki, reflexology, massage and Bowen, which I would swap with my friends for Reiki and yoga. E was nine years older, at 45 years, but he was a fit and healthy gardener and tree surgeon.

Both of us swam in the sea regularly throughout the year, and enjoyed cycling, running, and cliff walking together here in Guernsey. We also ate very healthily; I have a strong interest in nutrition, having studied a foundation course many years earlier, and made sure to cook meals from scratch using fresh produce. For ethical and health issues, I have avoided eating meat and dairy for years, and make sure to eat an otherwise varied diet.

If I'm honest, after five months or so, I knew that something was amiss. I'm fairly in touch with my body; in fact, it was hormonal imbalance and resulting depression that initially got me into yoga and Reiki, and which helped me to connect more deeply with my body and with its wisdom. Over the years, I have done a lot of work on myself, on all levels really, to try to heal the root cause of the hormonal imbalance and the depression, which had plagued me on and off for most of my late teens and twenties.

Like many women, I suffered from awful PMS, mood swings, and depression around the time of my period throughout my teens and twenties. It wasn't until I went to see a nutritionist that I even appreciated that my depression and low moods were cyclical in nature and linked to my menstrual cycle – I was totally disconnected from my menstrual cycle too; I just didn't recognise it had a cycle to it, beyond the fact that it made me fairly miserable. It sounds obvious now, but I was caught up in a masculine viewpoint of being strong and just getting on with it, rather than taking the time to understand the flow of my feminine energy.

I have since become intimately aware of my cycle, of its connection with the moon, and the manner in which my mood and energy levels change throughout the month. I was aware therefore – or so I thought – of when I was ovulating and when we should attempt to conceive. I thought I had everything worked out.

I also had a good understanding of my body. I had worked with a hormone specialist to balance my hormones, and more recently with an Ayurvedic doctor to enhance my fertility naturally. So, when I didn't fall pregnant, I knew something was wrong, albeit I didn't know what it was at the time.

But sadly, it didn't work, and the arrival of my monthly period was a source of great sadness and disappointment, the mark of being yet another month further away from fulfilling my dream of being a mother. As one month became three months, became six months, became nine months, well, it became soul destroying because you start questioning what you are doing wrong. And the whole time, your friends are getting pregnant and you try your best to be happy for them, but it just eats you up on the inside. Then the fear kicks in and you begin to question whether you'll ever get pregnant.

It's poignant really, because so many of us women spend some part of our lives trying not to get pregnant. When you do want to get pregnant, you assume it will just happen fairly painlessly, and when it doesn't, well, it's a kick in the teeth. And try as you might to keep the conception as conscious and as special as possible, truthfully, it becomes a bit mechanical and something that you have to do to try and achieve an outcome. Over time, it becomes emotionally charged too, because you become demanding of your partner, and they feel a pressure to perform. Trying for a baby in this controlled and slightly desperate way certainly wasn't a highlight in our lives, that's for sure!

REACHING OUT TO MY DOCTOR

In June, just before my 37th birthday, I finally went to see my doctor, and as I explained our predicament to her, I burst into tears at the frustration of it all. She was incredibly understanding and wasted no time in getting us into "the system". There were basic tests that both of us had to undertake, to try to gain an initial understanding of what may be amiss, and in the interim, we were encouraged to chill out and practice!

Sadly, those initial test results indicated that we had a significant problem in our ability to conceive. Further tests were required to establish what was going wrong, so we were immediately referred on to the Medical Specialist Group ("MSG") here in Guernsey. Healthcare in Guernsey is not free; you must pay to see a doctor, attend Accident & Emergency, or use an ambulance. However, should you require specialist care, you may be referred to the MSG by your doctor free of charge to see a specialist (the MSG have a contract with the States of Guernsey, who will pay for the treatment in certain cases). It wasn't until August, a few months later, when we finally had our first appointment with a gynaecological and obstetric specialist. Time takes on a new urgency when you are trying to conceive, and months tick by waiting for appointments. We were assigned to Mr Nzewi, who was new to Guernsey at the time, and very passionate about access to fertility treatment, which is not available directly on the island.

Mr Chuks Nzewi studied medicine in Nigeria before specialising in obstetrics and gynaecology in the UK. He worked for two years as a Senior Registrar at King's College Hospital London, and in 2008, was appointed as a Locum Consultant in the same hospital until moving to Guernsey.

His main areas of interest are Colposcopy, Gynaecological Ultrasound and Ambulatory Gynaecology, as well as minimal access surgery. He also tries to help women who experience fertility issues, and is passionate about making their access to fertility treatment as stress-free as possible, and is a keen advocate of making an initial round free of cost to the patient and covered by the States of Guernsey (the States of Guernsey currently don't pay for any fertility treatment). We felt we were in good hands.

It was at this initial appointment, as he looked at our results, that he shared the concern that we may never have children of our own. He was very matter of fact about it, because that is what the facts suggested, and he mentioned that there might be other options for bringing a child into our life if we were faced with that reality. But that said, there was a chance that the test results were flawed, so he sent us off for repeat tests, and in the interim, he advised us to do as much as we could to promote our fertility – healthy eating, exercise, less wine, more rest; the stuff we had been consciously trying to do anyway.

I tried to remain upbeat and fortunately, it was the summer, so we were kept busy with all that entails. However, all the worry did finally get the better of me. I know that worrying is a complete waste of energy, as it changes nothing, but it can be difficult not to worry sometimes. At the end of August, we joined friends at a house in France for a weekend of birthday celebrations. On that first night, sitting out on the lawn in the late afternoon sun, I drank far too much sparkling wine (so much for moderation!), got very upset, and told our friends what was going on, which was almost a relief really, because it gets to you, keeping it all bottled up inside.

I've had my fair share of challenges in life – that's what makes life "life" – but this was a particularly challenging time for both of us. For me, there was an all-consuming ache to become a mother and the pressure of my biological clock ticking, and for E, a pressure to help make that a reality. At that point, like quite a lot of other men we know, he could take or leave having a child. Certainly, in his twenties, he'd had every intention of having children, and he just assumed that that was where life would lead, but when it didn't, it wasn't so much that he accepted it, just that he never really gave it much thought. By the time I rocked up in his life in his early forties, talking about children, it threw him a bit, because by then, he'd reached an age where he was very settled in his way of living; he was used to his freedom and independence, and hadn't factored in children, or the change that they would necessitate. I'm grateful to his friends, who already had children, for encouraging him to be open and receptive to the idea. It's fair to say that he certainly didn't have quite the same burning desire as me, and in many respects, was just following my lead. But for me, it was all I could think about.

Needless to say (hangover aside), I felt much better for the release, and in many respects, it was good to have the support and understanding of our closest friends, who all live off island and who all have children of their own. They were really keen for E and I to have children too, and were jubilant that our relationship had finally made it to that point. They were all truly positive that one way or another, we would make it a reality.

Despite the sadness, and the underlying concern of it all, I, too, was still doing my best to keep positive. I just had this feeling that the challenge was all part of the process of whatever we both needed to go through, on an individual level and jointly, as part of the big Divine plan. During my whole life, but more so latterly, I had come to recognise that I was being continuously tested in patience, trust and faith, and really, this was just another test in all three. That didn't necessarily make it any easier, but I did feel supported on a spiritual level at least.

I appreciate that my take on the whole infertility issue may sound a little crazy to some of you. But this is how I have come to view life (when I remember!) from an elevated perspective – the belief, understanding and experience that things happen for a reason, that there is no good or bad per se, and that often, these challenges are blessings in disguise, because they provide you with an opportunity to grow spiritually and to deepen your connection with the Divine.

Time and time again, I have been reminded that our dreams – if we truly believe in them – can come true in the end, but rarely in the manner in which we intend. This is not to say that life has to be challenging to achieve our dreams, only that they often unfold in a way we can never have imagined. For me, it's always a reminder that we can't control these things – and that actually trying to control these things can lead us further away from the dream. Once a step has been made in the direction of the dream, the Universe conspires to assist; you've just got to listen to the heart, look for the signs, and never give up when the going gets tough – and (crucially) keep an open mind.

When I started to feel down, something told me to trust in the process, and that was good enough for me! But that is not to say that this trust wasn't continuously challenged. That is the nature of lessons – they will return again and again until you have recognised the teaching, and trust has always been a big one for me. And when I say trust, I don't mean some airy fairy notion of "putting it out there to the Universe" and sitting back and seeing what happens. I believe it needs greater grounding than this. Crystal clear intention and action-taking – and indeed some responsibility – when necessary, and trying to let go of the worry, fear and doubt that can cloud the mind and intuition.

OUR REFERRAL TO A FERTILITY CLINIC
Sadly, the second repeat set of test results we received during the first week of September came back identical to the first. I was expecting this, but it still came as a reality check because it proved that there were not any problems with the test data itself. We weren't quite sure what this meant at that stage because these were only basic tests, and while they indicated

that we were infertile as a couple, advances in science means that there are now options for those of us seemingly having trouble conceiving.

There was little more that Mr Nzewi could do for us therefore, other than refer us to a fertility clinic for further tests. At that point, he was trying to establish a better working relationship between MSG and Wessex Fertility Clinic in Southampton, to make it easier for Guernsey patients to undertake fertility treatment. All fertility care in Guernsey is private, so his intention was to try and help to reduce, at the very least, travel costs and inconvenience where possible, in respect of needing to go over to the UK simply for a scan or a blood test, as part of that treatment.

Luck was on our side in terms of the timing because we were fortunate to be included in the handful of patients who received appointments with Wessex on their first trip to MSG, so that we didn't even need to leave the island for our first consultation. Ironically, we were due to be off island that day, so I'm not entirely sure that it was any more cost effective for us, but nonetheless, we appreciated the contact in Guernsey and the ease with which this happened for us, albeit not until early October, which meant another month of waiting!

The consultant and nurses we saw were just great – very welcoming, positive and calming. The consultant studied our results, which showed that we didn't appear to have what we needed to conceive a baby, namely healthy sperm and eggs. However, she looked at us both, and saw that we were both healthy, with no obvious signs of hormonal imbalance (E had a beard, for example, and my skin was shining), and concluded that there was indeed hope. I guess she must get a feel for signs of hormonal imbalance and fertility issues upon greeting after years of working in the fertility world.

She proposed carrying out a more invasive procedure the following January, which would enable them to delve a little deeper and see with certainty whether we might have a chance (through IVF) of being able to conceive our own baby. Therefore, this procedure would, one way or another, seal our fate (well, our initial fate). In the interim, even though we still didn't know if IVF could help us to conceive, we needed to go through the "take-on" procedure with the clinic, to establish ourselves as patients in preparation for the additional invasive testing that was beyond the realms of specialist medical care in Guernsey. This meant the completion of a ton of forms and seemingly endless screening tests.

It was pretty full on, but we were delighted that we might have a chance of conceiving, even if that did mean using IVF. This was not as we had intended, of course, but a chance meant the world to us. We just hoped that the test results came back more positive next time and that we would be given the go ahead to actually begin IVF treatment. The motto was most definitely "trust in the process", and I vowed to try to do exactly that, allowing ourselves to be led down the path by the clinic and keep focusing on a positive outcome.

I remember very clearly completing those forms. I was sitting at a table with E and one of the nurses, who was guiding us through them, and in one of the forms, it asked us whether I would consent to my eggs and embryos (if created) being used for training purposes. I remember thinking, "Wow, this is real", and "It's not something I'd usually do, but I'm so desperate to be helped that anything I can do to help others in the future is worth doing, so yes, yes, yes, tick the boxes, yes."

Then there were questions about what would happen in the event of your death or mental incapacity, and what would happen to your eggs, embryos, and/or sperm, and whether you consent to your partner using them, or them being used for training purposes. We briefly discussed our position but, to be honest, we were so jubilant to even have this chance, to be talking about us having eggs, sperm, embryos and the like, that we were happy to sign away on this too: "Yes, yes, yes."

There were also forms to ascertain the welfare of the child, in which you had to disclose whether there was any serious violence or discord within your family environment, any drug or alcohol problems, and whether there are any aspects of your life or medical history that may pose a risk of serious harm to any child you might have, or anything that may impair your ability to care for such a child. In many respects, I considered that perhaps everyone should have to complete one of these forms before conceiving a child, not just those having IVF!

Then there was the concept of a multiple birth. Me being 37 years old by this time, it was recommended that we have two embryos implanted to increase our chances of success. It goes without saying that this would also increase the chances of us having twins and all the risks associated with multiple pregnancy. Still, I don't remember us giving this too much thought. Again, we were happy to go with the advice being given to us, and we ticked the box, "Yes, yes, yes, bring on the twins!!"

To me, that kind of summed up the situation. I never wanted to have fertility treatment – let's face it, who does – but here were Wessex providing some hope and I was willing to do all I could to make that hope a reality. That's the trouble with hope, isn't it? I know it's frowned upon in some spiritual circles, as it has no grounding or certainty, but hope gives life a reason to be lived, and that was good enough for me!

The fact we were even considering these options, and being primed to potentially have IVF, before we knew whether it was even possible to conceive in this manner, was uplifting in some way.

We didn't know too much about the IVF process at this point, because we weren't yet sure if it was an option for us. We were being prepared as if it would be, but had to wait for the results of the further invasive testing in the new year, before we could be sure this was the route for us. As all fertility treatment in Guernsey is private, we knew we would need to pay for any treatment, but at that point, until we knew what that treatment may entail, we had no clear idea on costs. We had no clear idea on anything really, other than the fact that Wessex were prepared to investigate us further and do what they could to potentially help us to conceive.

So after visiting the clinic, feeling positive, we had to embark on a number of screening tests, including Hepatitis B, Hepatitis C and HIV for each of us, and in addition, Chlamydia, Rubella antibodies and Anti-Mullerian Hormone (AMH) for just me. As you can appreciate, this all gets rather expensive and time-consuming, fitting in all the appointments. Not only that, but having a HIV test for the first time is quite a big deal, so there is some anticipation that comes with these additional screening tests. And some of these, the HIV for example, need to be repeated annually.

Chapter 2

Science and Spirituality of IVF

I remember reading a book about gentle mothering – in fact, it could very well have been entitled that – and in it, the "spiritual" author suggested that if you found out that you could not conceive naturally then perhaps this was the Universe's way of saying that you were not meant to conceive in the first place. Instead, she suggested that a level of acceptance should be reached and consideration should be given to adopting or finding a childfree path instead. She was very anti-IVF, and made it sound to me like it was the work of the Devil, simply because it wasn't a natural approach to conception and thus had no spiritual element to it.

The author's comments touched a nerve because I suspect in the earlier stages of my spiritual journey, I too had probably felt that science lacked the spirit. However, my perspective has shifted enormously since those earlier days. The Universe has continuously provided me with situations that have encouraged me to become a little more open-minded to science and the value it brings to life, and indeed, the fact that the spirit resides in all life, in scientists and in non-scientists too! Now here I was being given the opportunity to learn that IVF can be a spiritual journey – it is all about perspective.

IVF Explained

IVF itself stands for in vitro fertilisation: in vitro means "in glass". Essentially, it involves an egg being fertilised in a Petri dish in a laboratory under very carefully controlled conditions. It's quite amazing that science allows us to do this – and that's coming from someone who has never really been interested in science. I know not everyone agrees with this process, and perhaps that's the reason some people are secretive about going through IVF, but it's a miracle of science really.

In a woman's normal and natural cycle, usually, only one egg ripens within a growing follicle. An ovarian follicle is a fluid-filled sack that contains an immature egg. During ovulation, a mature egg is released from a follicle. If fertilised in one of the fallopian tubes (penetrated by sperm therefore), it travels to the uterus (womb), where – in theory – it implants and grows into an embryo, which becomes a blastocyst after five days (implanting into the uterine wall after six days), and eventually, becomes a foetus at week 11 of gestation (nine weeks after fertilisation).

With IVF, the aim is to cultivate multiple follicles to harvest many eggs, which are surgically extracted and fertilised with the sperm outside the body. If all goes well, the embryos are transferred into the woman's uterus three days later. Depending on the age of the woman, and because it is difficult to predict on day three which embryo is more likely to produce a pregnancy, it is not uncommon to have two embryos transferred in the hope that at least one will result in a live birth. The downside (depending on your perspective) is the risk of multiple births, which brings with it its own risks in terms of complications during pregnancy, and the emotional and financial demands this can place on couples.

For some couples, there is also the option of blastocyst transfer. A blastocyst is a highly-developed embryo that has divided many times, to a point where it is nearly ready to implant on the walls of the uterus. A blastocyst has come a long way from its beginning as a single cell. During maturation, an embryo rests inside a protective shell called a zona pellucid. You can think of this protective shell as being like a chicken egg, only that, unlike chicken eggs, the human embryo does not remain within a shell. Instead, the embryo hatches (breaks out of the shell) on the fifth or sixth day so that it can attach to the uterine wall (implantation). Just prior to hatching, an embryo becomes a blastocyst.

It is known that embryos that have developed to the critical blastocyst stage have a much greater chance of implanting successfully in the uterus and resulting in an on-going pregnancy. This is because these embryos have passed an important test. During the first few days, the embryo relies on the mother's egg for all its nutrients. However, in order to survive beyond day three or four, the embryo must activate its own genes. Not all embryos are successful. Those that are successful are understood to be more highly developed, healthier and stronger, and have a higher implantation rate when compared to day-three embryos.

It perhaps goes without saying that the ability to develop embryos to blastocyst stage allows clinicians to have greater certainty about which embryos are more likely to implant. Still, blastocyst-grading standards are still under development and it is difficult to accurately predict which blastocysts are destined for success. That said, if clinicians have the opportunity to allow embryos to develop into blastocysts before being transferred back into the uterus, then this is the preferred option.

Regardless of the science, I was also well aware from my holistic research that even if you have perfectly healthy blastocysts, your uterus may not provide the ideal environment for them to grow. It could be too acidic, for example, or the uterine lining not as thick as it is meant to be, thus preventing implantation. In short, there is absolutely no guarantee with IVF that the process will result in an on-going pregnancy – it is absolutely not an exact science!

Furthermore, IVF is a highly technical procedure, and I was only too well aware of the huge demands that the IVF drugs place on the body. I don't like to take pharmaceutical drugs at the best of times, and now, here I was hoping to be given the go ahead to start IVF and be prescribed huge dosages of them to supress my natural cycle, so that my body could be manipulated to stimulate ovulation and grow as many follicles as possible. A delicate hormonal balance would then be maintained artificially to allow the eggs to ripen but prevent ovulation from occurring before the clinic has a chance to retrieve the eggs – all controlled by high-dosage pharmaceutical drugs that have serious side effects.

The thing is, side effects or not, when this is your only option to conceive, you overlook all the stuff that would ordinarily have you saying, "No, no, no." It's not ideal but I was very aware that there wasn't a holistic path available to us. No amount of Ayurvedic herbs or Chinese medicine, let alone Bach Floral or Homeopathic remedies, were going to help us to conceive. That's not to say that they wouldn't complement the IVF process, but they alone were not going to create a baby. If they could, however, I would have chosen that option first. I don't feel that anyone should put their body, mind and soul through IVF until they have exhausted all other more natural options!

Preparing my mind, body and spirit for IVF

We now had a few months to prepare ourselves physically and – just as importantly – mentally and emotionally for what lay ahead. We were given an information sheet with pre-conceptual diet and lifestyle tips, which included the following:

Weight – Ideally, you should be as close as possible to the recommended weight for your height when trying for a baby. Apparently, being underweight or overweight can reduce your chances of conceiving.

Food – Studies have shown that foods and fertility are linked in both men and women. For that reason, you are encouraged to improve your diet three months to a year before conception. The Food Standards Agency recommends eating a variety of foods while trying to conceive, including:

- Fruit and vegetables – aim for at least five portions a day.
- Carbohydrate foods such as wholegrain rice and bread.
- Protein such as lean meat and chicken, fish, eggs and pulses.

- Fish – at least twice a week, including some oily fish, but not more than two portions of oily fish a week.
- Dairy foods such as milk, cheese and yoghurt.
- Iron-rich foods such as red meat, pulses, dried fruit, bread, green vegetables and fortified breakfast cereals, to help build up your resources of iron in preparation for pregnancy.

Supplements – Folic acid – this B vitamin has been linked to a lower rate of heart attacks, strokes, cancer and diabetes. It also reduces a baby's risk of being born with defects to the spinal cord, such as spina bifida. Make sure that the supplement you use does not contain Vitamin A or fish liver oil. In addition, it is good to eat folate-rich foods, such as dark green, leafy vegetables, citrus fruits, nuts, wholegrains, brown rice, fortified breads and cereals.

A supplement for pregnancy before you conceive, which for me was a vitamin preparation containing Selenium Coenzyme Q. Zinc might be beneficial for sperm health and production.

Alcohol – In terms of alcohol, the advice at that time was to drink no more than one or two units of alcohol once or twice a week.

Caffeine – Evidently, there is no consistent evidence to link caffeinated drinks to fertility problems, however, studies have shown that having more than 200 mg of caffeine per day may be linked to miscarriage and low birth weight.

To avoid – The Foods Standards Agency also recommends that women who are trying to conceive should also avoid the following:

- Too much Vitamin A – you need some Vitamin A, but too much during pregnancy could harm the baby.
- Fish containing mercury – high levels of mercury can harm an unborn baby's developing nervous system.
- Smoking – cigarette smoke contains harmful substances to eggs, sperm and developing embryos.

Excessive stress – This impacts the way the body functions. Prolonged periods of pre-conceptual stress should try to be avoided to help conception and improve fertility. A hectic, busy lifestyle with little time for relaxation, attention to diet or socialising is not advised. A less busy schedule generally promotes more happiness and a greater sense of wellbeing, leading to improved pre-conceptual health.

To be honest, we were already eating a healthy and balanced diet and we had made a conscious effort to reduce our alcohol intake. If anything, my major issue was stress and a hectic lifestyle. Ironic really, because as a yoga teacher and Reiki practitioner, you'd expect me to have a grip on this, but I am so passionate about yoga and Reiki that I have always kept myself very busy, sharing my love of both with others where I can, while also keeping up with the office day job, albeit part-time.

It was at this point that I read Zita West's marvellous book, *Fertility and Conception*, which I recommend to anyone interested in increasing their chances of conceiving, whether naturally or with intervention. It really is a fabulous book with lots of useful tips. And silly as it sounds, coming from a yoga teacher, it was reading this book that encouraged me to re-prioritise my time and incorporate daily meditation and Yoga Nidra into my hectic schedule.

I have always been a huge fan of Yoga Nidra, but the IVF made me dig deeper into the practice, and I would encourage anyone else with fertility issues to tap into this, as I have no doubt that it helped me enormously. Essentially, Yoga Nidra is a powerful meditation technique inducing complete physical, emotional and mental relaxation. During Yoga Nidra, one appears to be asleep, but the consciousness is functioning at a deeper level of awareness so that you are prompted throughout the practice to say to yourself mentally, "I shall not sleep, I shall remain awake."

I truly believe that absolutely everybody can receive some benefit from practicing Yoga Nidra – the yogic sleep – in their daily lives. But, in particular, I am an absolute firm believer that Yoga Nidra absolutely supports the IVF process. If there is one piece of advice I have for women preparing for, and going through IVF, it is this – prioritise a daily Yoga Nidra practice. There is a free one available on my website, but you will also find some fantastic free ones on the Yoga Nidra network (www.yoganidranetwork.org) too.

Before beginning Yoga Nidra, you make a Sankalpa, or a resolution for the practice. The Sankalpa is an important stage of Yoga Nidra as it plants a seed in the mind, encouraging healing and transformation in a positive direction. In practical terms, a Sankalpa is a declarative statement, resolution or intention, in which you vow to commit, to fulfil a specific goal, in this instance, to become pregnant with a healthy baby – "I am pregnant with a healthy baby."

Sankalpa or resolution holds a special and highly-esteemed place in the ancient yogic teachings. The concept of Sankalpa appears even as early as the Rig Veda, the most ancient of all the Vedic texts. This ancient concept of Sankalpa is based on the principle that your mind has measureless capacity to affect the quality and content of your life. As the Buddha said, "The mind is everything. What you think, you become." That said, it is also important that you feel how it would feel to achieve your Sankalpa, so there is some sensation related to it.

Furthermore, a Sankalpa provides you with an opportunity to notice any resistance that may be holding you back in creating/manifesting what you dream in your life. For example, if you are struggling to conceive and there is no recognised medical reason for this, working with Yoga Nidra may help you to realise any unconscious resistance you may have to getting pregnant or becoming a mother. You may not initially recognise this consciously, but over time, the unconscious element of this will become conscious (bring it out of the shadows) so that you are able to recognise it, if you see what I mean.

It is very powerful indeed and I cannot recommend this enough for anyone wishing to conceive. Not least, working with a Sankalpa, but also, just taking the time out for self-care and to rest – this in itself presents many physiological benefits, such as lowering of the heart rate and blood pressure, the release of lactate from the muscles that can cause anxiety and fatigue, a more restful night's sleep and, ultimately, a calming and unwinding of the nervous system, which is basically the foundation of the body's wellbeing. So you see, our physical health and sense of wellbeing can improve too, which can only help to support the fertility process.

I am absolutely certain that it was a combination of regular Yoga Nidra and daily seated meditation that helped me to maintain my sanity, stay focused and keep my spirits high during this time. I began to look forward to my daily meditation practice in particular, sitting at the end of my morning practice, just 20 minutes if I could, but this was more than enough to feel that it made a positive difference. I just felt clearer and calmer too; there is no doubt that my mind was stronger as a result of this, and I felt more level-headed, focused and less emotional somehow.

Needless to say, all of this certainly helped me to drop even deeper into my spiritual practice. I already had a daily mat-based yoga practice, but I carved out more time to make this an absolute priority, prior to the meditation and Yoga Nidra. For me, daily silence is essential too, and I'm fortunate in that I have the space to achieve this at home. So each day, I would take to my mat; sometimes, I needed to move my body and practice actively and other times, I needed to practice more gently, quietly or restoratively.

But what became very important to me during this time was prayer. Now I'm not religious, but as I've mentioned, I am spiritual, and for me, prayer has always been a way to connect more deeply with the Divine and with the angels, and now, here, I found it essential to my grounding and wellbeing to commune daily with these aspects of being and self. It made a huge difference to me to align on this level and feel even more supported by the Universe (however you define that), and therefore deepen my trust, and indeed faith, in the process and wherever it was leading us.

There were other things that I tapped into, including She Oak, which is one of the Australian Bush Flower Essences that is very beneficial in overcoming imbalances and bringing about a sense of wellbeing in females. It's a tincture that you take in water. It is said to benefit women who feel distressed about infertility and it helps, therefore, to remove personal blocks that prevent conception. For me, this was essential, doing what I could to be ready and receptive on all levels, ensuring that I had addressed all aspects of my being, not simply the physical, but the mental, emotional and spiritual too.

I also started Acupuncture. I had heard that while there is no scientific evidence to support the link, there does appear to be some correlation between acupuncture and successful IVF. If nothing else, it enabled me to take time out of my schedule to lie down and chill out, although I did notice a positive uplift in my energy levels after each session. I complemented this a little with Reiki, massage and reflexology; fortunate, as I was to be able to swap this for yoga and Reiki with friends.

Reiki, in particular, was hugely supportive to me at the time, as it has been at many other challenging times in my life. The word "Reiki", which is Japanese and pronounced "ray-key", means "universal life force energy". It refers to an ancient hands-on healing art developed by Dr Mikao Usui in Japan in the early 1900s for personal spiritual development and the passing of healing energy onto others.

Reiki is best known in the West as a gentle but powerful system of hands-on healing, which can easily be learned by anyone to heal themselves, others, plants and animals. It works on all levels – mental, emotional, physical and spiritual – and can create a more resourceful state of being, helping people to relax, feel a greater connection to all of life, and remember the fullness of who they are, fulfilling their true potential in life.

Treatments and spiritual practice aside, life carried on much as usual for the rest of that autumn. I kept myself busy with a combination of my existing yoga teaching and Reiki channelling schedule, and the office job. At that time, the company I worked for was being sold to a larger company in the UK, and as company secretary, this meant many more hours in the office than usual – a welcome distraction from our fertility issues and it helped me to earn extra money to be able to pay for the treatment (more on that later!).

Before too long, it was Christmas, and we decided to make the most of this as we were quite certain – positivity and all – that this would be our last Christmas as just the two of us. We decided that we would enjoy ourselves and have lots of fun. We even took ourselves away for a night of partying in London, to kind of get it out of our system, knowing that from 1st January, it was absolutely all about IVF and conceiving, and we were feeling really focused that 2013 would be our year. It was just a waiting game really until the next round of tests in late January.

Chapter 3
The Clinic and Testing

Our appointment to attend Wessex Fertility Clinic in Southampton for the invasive procedure that would, one way or another, determine our future, was booked for mid-January. It was exciting and I couldn't wait to just get on with it now. I was still feeling positive and had begun the New Year completely focused and intent on a successful process, so 2013 was – as far as I was concerned – all about faith, trust, fertility and getting pregnant.

Living on Guernsey, where fog is always an issue, we flew over to Southampton the evening before the appointment to ensure that we wouldn't miss it. At the time, E was a member of the Best Western, so we booked ourselves into the Chilworth Manor House in Southampton, which turned out to be a bit of a gem and I would highly recommend to others who have to go to Wessex.

We didn't get there until late in the evening, and while the hotel itself is a little quirky in layout, it wasn't until the morning that we got to see that the gardens were something else. It may sound silly but the opportunity to calm ourselves in nature was well received, because despite our best efforts, we were both feeling a little anxious. So after E had eaten breakfast and I'd taken that time to practice yoga on my mat instead, we ventured out into the grounds of the hotel and did exactly what we needed, grounded ourselves a little.

The hotel is located within 12 acres of beautifully landscaped grounds and is right next door to a conservation area. It's truly stunning. I will always remember our wanderings that morning. It was one of those bright, crisp and very cold winter days. The ground was frozen hard, there was a layer of thin ice on the pond, and our breath smoked in the air. It was ever so quiet and peaceful, just us and the odd dog walker, and the sound of our feet crunching across the hard and icy earth.

We came upon a collection of tall cypress trees, which had been planted in a circle and created what looked like a sacred site within. We later discovered that this was a deer circle used to herd the deer, but to me, it seemed more appropriate as a ceremonial area, and clearly others felt the same, as there was evidence of a fire in the middle. I was rather uplifted by our find and took myself right to the centre to feel its beautiful central energy for some ritual yoga and prayer; I could almost feel the eyes of the wood sprites upon us as we walked away!

Back towards the Manor House itself, we came across a very old cedar tree with an absolutely enormous trunk. It's understood that the tree is approximately 420 years old, which is some age; apparently the oldest cedar tree in the UK. Well this was a bonus for us; there's nothing quite as grounding as hugging a tree, and especially one that is that many years old – wow. Can you imagine the changes that tree has seen, and all the time it's just been standing there, doing its thing – incredible! You can learn a lot by spending time with the trees, and it made me consider that we too just have to do our thing, wherever it leads.

TESTS

We took a taxi to the clinic and were surprised to find it a little incongruous, set in a residential area, and back from the road a little, with no evidence from the outside that it's a fertility clinic as such. It made me realise that there still is – or was at that point in time – such stigma about fertility and fertility clinics, and yet to me, it just seemed to be something you did if you couldn't conceive naturally, no big deal.

Still, I have a dear friend who had gone through IVF to conceive her first born and was very keen that no one knew that she and her partner needed to have IVF, and so they tried to keep it a secret for fear of what others may think. I'd never really understood this myself, because I'd never considered it as an issue. However, seeing the clinic building made me consider that maybe I was the one who had got it wrong. Perhaps there was a need to be secretive about this way of bringing new life into the world, and perhaps I would encounter negativity if I mentioned it to others.

Then again, it crossed my mind that maybe I needed to be the one who didn't worry about what other people would think. I could help others going through a similar thing and also assist a little in removing some of the stigma that still exists. I don't feel that it needs to be secretive, there is certainly nothing to be ashamed or embarrassed about, the outcome is the same regardless of the process, so what does it matter if people find out your children were conceived through IVF? It was certainly too late for us anyhow; we'd told most of our close friends that we were having trouble conceiving naturally and they knew we were meeting with the clinic for further investigations.

Entering the clinic, I noticed that the walls of the entrance hall and either side of the stairs leading up to the reception area were covered in photos of babies who had presumably been conceived through IVF at the clinic. I guess it helped to reinforce the reason we were there and I hoped that one day, a picture of our own biological baby might also make it on to the walls, as proof that IVF really does work, and that it's possible for dreams to come true!

The staff at the clinic were very friendly and welcoming, and we took our seats to wait for the appointment. It is only a small clinic, or at least it was back then (not that I have a comparison), and the small waiting area was filled with a few other anxious faces. It was strange to think that we were all there for one common goal, to conceive, and yet presumably, all of us were having different complications that were preventing this from happening naturally. It gave me a sense that fertility issues are more common than I may have previously realised, and that we were certainly not alone in our quest for conception.

There was a part of me that couldn't believe that we were here. It was all so new to us at that point, a whole other world that we needed to learn about. I'll never forget working with a Reiki client a few years earlier who was having trouble conceiving and was undertaking IVF. That was my first real exposure to anyone having IVF and I remember it as if it was yesterday. Something about it made me take note, not least because it was even more secretive back in the day, but because I really felt that the Reiki would help her conceive, and because it seemed so stressful for her, and now, here I was going through the same process myself – it's funny how the Universe leaves signs along the way.

Still, at that point, we weren't entirely sure that we could conceive through IVF either and this was the reason we were here at Wessex in the first place. Our earlier test results in Guernsey suggested that we didn't have what was needed between us to conceive our own biological baby. However, our consultant was fairly confident that with some further testing – invasive testing at that – they could find what was needed, so here we were for that invasive testing.

THE FIRST PIECE OF GOOD NEWS

The testing was focused on E at this particular appointment, and I shall never forget the moment that our friendly consultant joined me later on that morning in the then-empty waiting room. She excitedly told me the good news, that the results of the testing were positive and that while a medical condition (which could not be treated and therefore was of little interest to the clinic or to anyone else for that matter!) would prevent us from conceiving naturally, there was every chance that we could conceive a biological child through IVF. I could have jumped with joy – what a relief! Instead, I went outside and telephoned my parents and duly burst into tears conveying the good news!

I think often, people forget that there are two people involved in conception, at least in terms of requiring both healthy sperm and healthy eggs, and when IVF is mentioned, people tend to presume it's because the woman has fertility issues. Studies indicate that in the UK, infertility affects at least 20-25% of couples who are of reproductive age. This means that 1 in 5 couples you know will be affected by some degree of infertility. Of the couples having IVF treatment, 50% will be due to male infertility and 50% due to female infertility.

These are interesting statistics and I have become aware that male infertility is often another reason that couples keep their IVF journey a secret. I guess it is more of an issue for men, from an ego perspective, than it is for women, to have to admit that they are unable to impregnate their partner naturally. In addition, the infertile man may often feel a lot of guilt that their healthy partner has to pump herself full of strong pharmaceutical drugs and go through the stress of IVF, to fulfil her dream of becoming a mother, when there is actually nothing wrong with her, fertility wise.

E and I have certainly gone through our own angst with this, and whilst from an IVF perspective, we present as an infertile couple, we are fortunate that the sperm provided by E were good quality. From my side, while tests suggested that I was ovulating, we wouldn't know until we began the IVF treatment whether my eggs would be of a sufficient quality to create a baby. Only time would tell.

Sitting in the waiting room awaiting E, I reflected on the irony of our plight. I had spent years and an awful lot of time and money trying to balance my hormones naturally. At the age of 17, I had developed an eating disorder that had caused my periods to stop for a few months, and ever since then, I had struggled a little with PMS, which became much more intense during my twenties and led to bouts of all-consuming depression. It was PMS and the depression (as well as running the London Marathon and the detrimental effect this had on my body) that led me to yoga and Reiki in the first place back in 2003.

I have worked with both yoga and Reiki intensely and extensively over the years, so too Ayurveda, homeopathy and other complimentary therapies, to help to heal the root cause of the hormonal imbalance, naturally. I haven't suffered with PMS or the bouts of all-consuming depression for a good few years as a result of this healing work. And now, here I was, about to pump my body full of very strong and very high dosages of pharmaceutical drugs, to control and manipulate my hormonal balance, so that I could conceive new life in a test tube in a very clinical environment. It certainly wasn't the stuff of dreams.

However, despite the nature of IVF, I was still feeling very positive and extremely excited about the fact we now had the opportunity to try it. I believe when you've had to consider that this may not happen, it's just a relief to know that there is a way, a possibility, some solidity or grounding, to the hope that you've been feeling. I recognise that I am lucky and I need to stress that point, because I know other couples, friends, family and students who have not been so lucky, who cannot, even with the help of IVF, conceive naturally (at least not their own biological child), and I appreciate that that can be a heart-breaking reality.

While I am a believer that everything happens for a reason, I do struggle a bit with understanding why some people are able to procreate and others do not have that opportunity physiologically. Accepting that you cannot have your own biological children must be tough. I don't know what we would have done if we had found ourselves faced with that reality – just it even being a possibility was enough to challenge me. I have seen those who cannot conceive go on to adopt or take donor eggs or sperm, and others decide to take a different path in life and immerse themselves in their pets or nieces and nephews instead.

I have seen others become angry and bitter to the point that they cannot bring themselves to communicate with those who have children or who have managed successful IVF cycles. I guess we each have our own way of dealing with what life throws at us; some manage to find some peace and others struggle to find the level of acceptance required to experience this. I have a huge amount of respect for people who have to go through this and cannot imagine the strain it places on relationships, let alone on one's faith.

For me, my faith was strengthened as the consultant told me that we were good to start the treatment when we were ready, and that this would involve using ICSI (Intra-Cytoplasmic Sperm Injection). In conventional IVF, at least 100,000 sperm must be placed with each egg to have a realistic chance of achieving fertilisation. ICSI treatment involves the injection of a single sperm directly into each egg, which is really rather incredible when you think about it. The treatment leading up to and after ICSI is identical to the conventional IVF cycle.

I was keen to get going with the treatment as soon as possible and the consultant was happy for me to start on my next cycle in February. This felt right somehow, not least because it was the earliest we could begin and I am impatient, but more so because it was the beginning of spring, and from my perspective, this was important energetically. Spring is all about new beginnings as nature begins to awaken again from her winter sleep and new life arrives daily, so that you can feel the lighter vibrancy of this "new life" energy in the air.

Even Zita West, in her fabulous book, *Fertility & Conception* writes, "*In my experience, IVF seems to work better in spring and summer, the time for growth and renewal within the natural cycle. In autumn and winter, nature is dormant and the body needs rest and sleep rather than action. If time is on your side and you have the choice, opt to begin treatment in spring rather than winter.*" So I guess there must be something in it; intuitively, it just felt right for us regardless.

Keeping positive

I was well aware that it was vitally important for me to maintain positive thinking, and with that, mental balance and clarity. Positive thinking is essentially a mental attitude in which you expect good and favourable results – it is a process of only allowing thoughts that create and transform energy into a positive reality. This works on the understanding that we manifest situations, events and conditions in our lives based on the thoughts we are thinking; thus, the more positive the thought, the more positive the situation created in one's life.

Therefore, I tried to pay attention to my thinking and notice when I was slipping into either negative thinking or self-pity, and with that, I would try (try, try) to let the negative thoughts go and focus on being more positive instead. It is not necessarily an easy process but it can be very interesting as you start to recognise habitual thinking patterns and negative tendencies. It becomes easier with practice, and with this new-found awareness, one realises that we are the creators of our own destiny, depending upon the nature of our thinking.

I knew it was essential to prepare for IVF, to give the process the best possible chance of success, and I had been doing this already, but now it was time to up the stakes, so to speak. I was also aware that it was vitally important to maintain the positivity and to believe in the IVF process. It may not be ideal, it was certainly not the way I had imagined or indeed dreamt of conceiving, but it was a way, and I was very aware that I needed to seek out any resistance I had to this and let it go if I was going to stand a chance of getting pregnant.

Sadly, I have witnessed this resistance resulting in repeated failed IVF cycles for some couples. It comes back to one of the best pieces of advice I have ever been given, from a good friend who has successfully conceived through IVF. She told me that under no circumstances was I to ever give in to self-pity during the IVF process. I have found this to be incredibly true, because the moment the self-pity sneaks in, the more you give your power away and lose your focus on the positive outcome.

This is not to say that self-pity didn't sneak in at times, or at least, the opportunity to recognise it appeared. Despite all my positivity and excitement, a week after returning to Guernsey from our Wessex appointment, I had a bit of a down moment. I had to go to MSG, here in Guernsey, to meet with a local nurse to pick up my prescription for the drugs, run through the treatment schedule, and be shown how to inject myself. It was while she was demonstrating the two different ways in which you inject yourself with the medication that I had been prescribed that I burst into tears.

I had done so well up until then, and had managed to remain fairly level-headed, but all of a sudden, the reality dawned on me that I was really going to do this; I was going to consciously inject myself with incredibly strong pharmaceutical drugs. I know it sounds silly, because I knew this was the only way I would achieve the outcome I desired, and I thought I was OK with it, but all of a sudden, I wasn't OK with it after all. I was only too aware that some of the prescribed medication has side effects as serious as recognised links to uterine, breast and ovarian cancer – not ideal that you are consciously injecting that risk into your own body!

As a result, I found myself questioning what I was doing. However, I knew that I had little choice if I wanted to conceive, and with that, I was a little saddened at the seeming injustice of it all, and the self-pity crept in. How come it was so easy for so many of my friends and family members to conceive naturally, and why was it so difficult for E and I? What was the Universe playing at? It all just seemed so unfair. I was going to have to do the very thing I had spent years standing against (here was the lesson, right?!), not least the pumping of my body with drugs, but also accepting allopathic (medical) care and allowing my body to be viewed as just that, without much of a heart or soul, just another statistic, another woman who needs intervention to conceive. I was heartbroken really.

The nurse was very kind and softened the blow as best she could. The trouble is, there is a degree of pity involved in this whole sorry process, because IVF is absolutely not an exact science, and as a nurse said to me years later, it's a little bit like taking a roll of the dice. You can do all you are told to do by the clinic, but this still may not result in a successful pregnancy and as such, you are often pitied. However, I suppose it was this bit, this little flaw in the science of it all (in that it wasn't an exact science) that gave me a reason to bring my heart and soul into the process, and helped to strengthen my faith.

Here was my chance to truly tap into my spiritual approach to life, and also to the complimentary world, which is called that for good reason, as it compliments allopathic care and healing. So, in many respects, I began to see IVF as another mission, a little like healing from depression, or the eating disorder, and all the other physical, mental and emotional challenges life has presented to me. And believe you me, IVF demands of you, not just physically, but most definitely emotionally and mentally. And for many, whether they realise it or not, it has a potentially huge spiritual element to it too.

I guess it was in that moment, in tears with the nurse at MSG, that I came to recognise what my friend meant when she had told me not to buy into self-pity. And it was in that moment that I resolved to let go of any resistance I had to the IVF process, to the drugs and the allopathic care, and all the stuff I don't usually invite into my life, and just surrender to it. While IVF was not on my list of ways one connects more deeply to spirit, I was coming to recognise that in doing IVF, one has the opportunity to connect more deeply to spirit in the lessons it provides – and the ability to surrender (and therefore let go of the way you believe things should be) is a huge lesson in this.

I decided that while I would read about the risks associated with the drug treatment on the patient information sheets provided by the clinic, I would not research them in depth on the Internet. Nor would I be consumed by the side effects, other than just recognising what I needed to look out for in case I had an adverse reaction to them. I would simply trust that the Universe had my back, so to speak, and do what needed to be done from a place of love rather than fear. This in itself, I was realising, is a huge lesson too.

I also felt it important to have some understanding of what they were meant to be doing to me, in terms of being able to feel and recognise this in my body – for example, were they shutting my system down or stimulating it? I am well aware that the mind plays a pivotal role in the workings of our body, so the more I could do mentally to support the process, the better. I felt that if I was resistant to the drugs mentally then there was a chance that the drugs would not work as effectively as if I just embraced them and allowed them to do what they needed to do to achieve the intended outcome.

Visualisation

It is my experience that positive thinking can be further helped by visualisation, and in particular, vision boards. Basically, a vision board involves you putting together a sheet of photos or images of whatever it is you would like to attract into your life. For example, if you would like to become pregnant and have a healthy baby then you might stick images on your vision board of you with a pregnant tummy and you holding a healthy baby – you may need to do some cutting and pasting!

It is important that there is an image of you somewhere on the vision board so that there is a link between the images and you. It is also important that you feel what it would be like to manifest your intentions in your life – or at least how you imagine you would feel!

Vision boards have always been very powerful for me in terms of being clear, visually, about what I would like to attract into my life and the positive feelings attached to the images (and the ability to manifest accordingly).

Once you've finished your vision board, you should put it somewhere you may see it regularly, so that you can remind yourself what it is you are trying to manifest in your life. The process of putting a vision board together may also help you to recognise any unconscious resistance you may be harbouring, and that may unintentionally block the IVF/conception process. Such resistance may include you feeling that you don't deserve to get pregnant and fulfil a dream, or that you are unworthy of bringing new life into the world.

Another thing that really helped me with the visualisation was placing a figurine of a family (man with arm around woman, holding a baby in her arms) on my altar, and practicing yoga, meditating and praying in front of it. I found this really helpful in being absolutely clear about what it was I was trying to bring into my life and seeing it daily. It was the same with the fertility bracelet that I bought a good six months before we began the IVF process and wore daily. This contained rose quartz, moonstone, pearls and rhodonite – all crystals that help to promote fertility, and which I hoped would put out a clear message to the Universe!

OTHER ELEMENTS HOLDING YOU BACK

Through my healing work, I've also noticed that some ladies have unconscious resistance as a result of their upbringing. For some, they may have had a difficult relationship with their mother, so they worry whether they can be a good mother themselves, or they are so busy mothering other family members that they don't have the energy necessary to focus on being a mother and creating a family of their own.

Others are bitter about something that has happened to them in their childhood, and carry the victim and blame mentality into adulthood. Unconsciously, they create some internal resistance to happiness – if having a baby would make them happy then on some level, they resist this, so they can continue to play out the victim role and blame others for their continued unhappiness rather than taking personal responsibility. Healing work is often required to address these deep-seated issues, so that the individual can forgive and move on.

FOCUSSING ON HEALTHY EGGS

After seeing the nurse at MSG, I only had a week or so to wait until I was due to begin the treatment in earnest, so I tried to settle into my zone. I was already practicing yoga and meditating daily, and doing Yoga Nidra where I could, but now, I began trying to incorporate an 18-minute version of this healing and relaxation technique into my daily schedule, and I started working with a new Sankalpa.

For me now, it wasn't so much about getting pregnant (although of course, this was still my intended outcome), but more so about producing quality healthy eggs. I was determined to live, breathe and visualise healthy eggs! Without healthy eggs, there was little chance of me getting pregnant, so this seemed an important stage in the process, and to me, it was all about stages and dealing with each in turn. Thus, my Sankalpa now was, "I produce good quality and healthy eggs."

A woman is born with all of the eggs she will ever possess, and egg health is understood to be the cornerstone of fertility. Thus, they need to be nourished to be able to mature, ovulate, fertilise, implant and result in a baby. The amount and quality of the eggs is genetically determined and reduces over the years, although the environment that eggs grow in can be affected by lifestyle factors, just like any other cell in the body really.

What I never realised was the fact that the egg cell is the largest significant human cell in the body and is just visible to the naked eye. It is also the roundest cell, and therefore, has the largest volume in relation to its surface. Sperm cells, on the other hand – what a lesson IVF offers in biology too – are the smallest of significant human cells and are the straightest cells. Egg cell and sperm are each other's opposite therefore, large versus small, round versus straight, cytoplasm versus nucleus.

However, while the differences between sperm cells and egg cells are great, opposites attract and they belong together. I find this fascinating, because we see this at work in life, not least in terms of how people come together to form a relationship, complementing each other with their opposing attitudes and approaches to life (she's social, he's not; she brings him out of himself, he calms her down, so they balance each other out, for example), but also energetically.

In Reiki certainly, there is a symbol we use that contains the energy of the universal male and the universal female.

The universal male, "Shiva", is represented by a straight line (like sperm then!), whereas the universal female, "Shakti", is represented by a spiralled circle (the roundness of the egg). We see this concept of the universal male and universal female in yoga too – opposing energies brought together to create union.

It is the same with electricity – not that I know too much about this, but I do know that there have to be two poles, positive and negative, to allow the energy to flow. If one of these poles is missing, then there is no circuit and nothing works. So it's the same here with the sperm and the egg; we need both to create new life, the universal male and the universal female.

An egg lives for up to 24 hours, which is a short timeframe, and it needs to be as healthy as it can be during this time. In addition, the right hormones are required in the right amount at the right time during the menstrual cycle to grow, mature and ovulate an egg. During IVF, the hormonal levels are manipulated with synthetic drugs to increase the chances of a woman growing, maturing and ovulating at least one good quality egg. There is much we can do to assist this process and increase the chances of good egg health, including:

- Reducing sugar consumption;
- Eating a diet rich in antioxidants to neutralise free radicals (which damage cells);
- Ensuring adequate levels of B vitamins, zinc, Omega 3 and Essential Fatty Acids;
- Eating a healthy diet and avoiding foods contained within cans or packaged in plastic (which contain toxins and affect egg health);
- Maintaining a healthy weight;
- Drinking plenty of water;
- Ensuring adequate sleep and rest;
- Taking adequate exercise especially yoga and walking;
- Reducing stress levels;

- Eliminating activities and people who exhaust and take from you;
- Making positive lifestyle choices.

Also, a number of studies have been conducted that have found a positive link between acupuncture and successful IVF cycles for some people. It's possible that this is due to the fact that acupuncture can help to increase blood flow to the pelvic area and the ovaries, and if the blood flow is good, then more nutrients are able to get through and increase the health of eggs. In addition, acupuncture may promote a sense of relaxation and positive thinking, which can improve a person's overall sense of wellbeing and increase the chances of pregnancy.

I had already been receiving regular acupuncture, and certainly felt a benefit in my general sense of wellbeing and energy levels, so I increased these sessions to weekly and made them the main focus of my complimentary work. I had also been receiving regular Reiki, reflexology and massage in the lead up to the IVF, and increased the frequency of these to help balance, ground and relax me, and increase my general sense of wellbeing and mental stability. I was fortunate, I should add, in being able to exchange many of the holistic sessions (which were given by friends) for yoga classes with me.

There were lots of other things I did to prepare myself for the IVF, and you can read about these on the self-help page on my website under "fertility issues". This meant that, by the time it came around to beginning the treatment, I felt that I had done all that I could to prepare myself, and now it was a matter of getting on with it. For the first time in a good 18 months, my period could not have come soon enough. I positively welcomed it as it brought with it a new stage on the journey to conceive, and with that, the beginning of the IVF antagonist cycle.

An antagonist cycle is a process used during IVF to prevent premature ovulation. It uses certain drugs (explained more thoroughly later) to stop the release of luteinising hormone and follicle-stimulating hormone. Both of these are important hormones that direct the menstrual cycle and ovulation. Antagonists quickly block the receptor (the place that receives signals from the body) that tells the body to release the luteinising hormone and the follicle-stimulating hormone.

By "turning off" the body's natural hormones, they are less likely to interfere with IVF medications. The IVF drugs then take over by directing egg maturation, egg release and preparing the uterine lining for embryo implantation. The advantage of the antagonist cycle is that treatment can be tailored closely to one's individual needs. Not that I really had much of a choice; the clinic decided that this was the path for us and we felt confident in their choice, based on their expertise and experience.

Chapter 4
Scans and Injections

I don't think you can ever get used to having transvaginal ultrasound scans as such, but by the time I began the IVF antagonist cycle, I had already had two of them, and I tried not to think too much about it. I just had to consider that these scans are all part of the process to achieve a certain outcome. It was all about the outcome after all, and staying focused on this helped enormously. Not to say they weren't intrusive, they're incredibly intrusive, but I just couldn't allow myself to dwell.

E was great and attended every specialist appointment with me. I just felt that I needed the moral support, and he felt that it was important to be part of the process too. We were trying to conceive after all, and that involved bits from both of us, so we gave it our all: body, mind and soul. Thus, after my period started, I had to go to MSG for a transvaginal ultrasound scan of my ovaries to check for cysts before I could begin the treatment.

I wasn't expecting the specialist to find any, and he didn't, but it is still a necessary part of the programme before you can be given the go ahead to start the medication. It is perhaps worth sharing here that there was a time when I did have cysts on my ovaries. I share this only because I know that others experience this, and cysts can make it tricky to conceive naturally and can complicate the IVF process (or so I believe). I managed to heal my cysts naturally, and it was a lesson for me, not only in terms of how we can hold unprocessed emotions in our bodies, but how we may heal these holistically.

My ovaries

As I have mentioned previously, I developed an eating disorder when I was 17 years old. It began with me starving myself, which caused my periods to stop. Then when I went to university, later that same year, I fell into the nasty trap of starving and then binging, so that I actually put on weight, and every day, my life was consumed with what I was eating. When I look back, it was exhausting, and it went on for too many long years. The trouble is that once an eating disorder has taken root, it's very difficult to let it go.

By the time I was approaching my mid-twenties, I knew that something had to change. I was still caught in a cycle of obsessing about what I ate and starving and binging myself in equal measure, while exercising excessively. Essentially, I didn't really like myself very much, and my relationship with food, the PMS and depression I experienced were all-consuming at times and utterly exhausting.

Fortunately, after running the London Marathon, I found yoga. My body was in a mess and someone mentioned to me that yoga might help. I had already read that yoga could help with PMS and depression, so it seemed to make sense to give it a try. I had nothing to lose. So that's what I did, and the rest is history really. Yoga made me feel better. For the first time in a long time, I was encouraged out of my head and into my body.

Without a doubt, yoga saved my life. It was through yoga that I came to discover Reiki, which was truly life changing for me, and also brought with it a world of healing, crystals, angels and good nutrition. I started seeing a local nutritionist, who was just brilliant. She was very "no-nonsense" and prescribed a diet and supplements that made an incredible difference to how I felt, I couldn't believe it!

Until that point, I ate what I ate depending on what I felt it would do to my weight, opposed to what I felt it would do for my health. It was incredible really, to finally understand that much of my PMS symptoms were due to my diet, and I came to realise that we truly are what we eat. With that, there was a huge shift in my relationship with food and with myself, but sadly, eating disorders do not disappear overnight, and there are always trigger events.

A trigger event for me was immersing myself in the Australian Byron Bay yoga scene when I was approaching

30 years old, which was full of skinny yogis, who ate very limited diets under the guise of being healthy. I tried many different diets, from a vegetarian diet to a raw food vegan diet, from juicing to a fruit-only diet. After a stay of five months one time, I returned home to Guernsey the skinniest I had ever been, my periods had stopped, and once again, my mind was utterly consumed with my weight.

I knew, without a doubt, that something had to change. My Reiki Master happens to be a hormone expert, so I undertook some saliva testing to investigate the lack of periods and the results indicated I had polycystic ovaries. I went to my doctor, who took a good look at me and disagreed with the diagnosis, as I wasn't overweight (quite the opposite), and I didn't have spots or excess hair on my face. Still, she sent me for a scan, and sure enough, this showed that I had a whole heap of tiny cysts covering both my ovaries. There was no treatment for this as such; the doctor just mentioned that it might make it trickier for me to conceive, so they would address the matter then.

I decided I wasn't going to wait for that potential outcome and set out to heal myself naturally, following a treatment schedule given to me by my Reiki Master, which used a whole heap of supplements and progesterone cream. However, I recognised that there was an emotional element to this condition (and the underlying eating disorder, which I didn't mention to anyone and no one raised with me; I guess they just assumed I was naturally skinny!) and I took myself off to Jersey to see a lady who offered Brandon Bays' *The Journey* sessions. It was one of those things I just felt drawn to do and it was actually very interesting.

Essentially, the lady guided me on a journey to my ovaries to see what was really going on for them. I was surprised to see that eating away at my ovaries, quite literally, was a resentment I had been holding on to for some time, since I was 17 years old actually, and an incident that I believe may have triggered my eating disorder in the first place. It's funny what we hold onto in our lives, and the manner in which we literally hold this somewhere in our body, leading to disease. It's definitely not a good thing to find yourself doing, especially when it affects the organs of the body, as it was doing here for me.

Initially, I was surprised that this particular episode and my reaction to it had ruled my life for so many years, and it was with some relief that I was now able to address it, make peace with it and move on from it. It taught me a huge lesson, however, in how our thoughts and unexpressed emotions can be held within the tissue of the body, and affect our physical and mental health - here eating disorders are mental disorders that manifest physically. It was also a huge lesson in how we can heal ourselves if we are ready to dig deep and get down to the nitty gritty of it.

I complemented *The Journey* with Ayurveda. Meaning "the science of life", it is exactly that, viewing health in four dimensions of physical, sensory, mental and spiritual, and is centred on preventative medicine and bringing a person back to balance. It shows how an imbalance in one part of a person's being will affect them in another, i.e. if a person isn't being true to their life path (dharma) then physical and mental illnesses can arise, which cannot be effectively treated with modern medicines but can be helped by Ayurveda.

Ayurveda uses elemental medicine, which means that they balance out earth, fire, water, air and ether, in the body. These are divided into three doshas: Vata, Pitta and Kapha, which are the basis of a person's constitution and also the factors that can create imbalances. Ayurveda places great emphasis on diet, lifestyle, yoga, meditation, massage and herbal medicines to bring a person back to health and keep them there.

My Ayurvedic doctor, a truly lovely Sri Lankan lady called Dr Deepika, who is based near Gatwick, prescribed a nourishing diet that would suit my natural constitution; this alone was healing, simply eating, that is! She also gave me some herbs to take and I attended the clinic for some treatments, all of which were aimed at healing the root cause of the imbalance, which was presenting itself as cysts and PMS. The treatment certainly shifted how I felt, and soon, my periods started again and eventually synced with the moon, and I was aware that I was ovulating once more too.

I have pretty much followed the Ayurvedic diet for my constitution ever since then. It fascinates me because when I move away from this, I notice that my fire element gets out of balance, and with that, all sorts of changes occur, very subtle, but enough for me to now know when things have become imbalanced. Ayurveda has been as life changing for me as yoga and Reiki, there is no doubt. It resonates on every level and I really like the Ayurvedic doctor I see. She has counselled me spiritually and has certainly towed me into line when it has been necessary over the years.

The combination of all this healing work helped to heal my ovaries and this was one of the reasons I was surprised we were not able to conceive from the outset, because I had done some Ayurvedic work prior to us trying to conceive to prepare my body for conception. Still, we were where we were, and about to embark on the IVF process, with the go ahead from both our specialist and from the clinic to begin the injections the following day. Wow, it was absolutely really happening, we were one step closer to realising our dream.

Injections

The next day after my scan, I started injecting. Only that I didn't do the injecting. I couldn't inject myself; it just didn't feel right somehow, so E did it for me. He was happy to do it as it happens, not to cause me pain (obviously) but to be involved in the process. I found it easier leaving him to sort out this side of the treatment, measuring the quantity of drugs that needed to be injected daily and injecting this into my tummy, trying his best to ensure minimal bruising.

Fortunately, Wessex provided me with a comprehensive treatment booklet, which clearly detailed every step of the treatment, not only providing visual charts to help make sense of what happened when, but also listed out each step of the treatment schedule and included a timetable that had been filled out specifically for me and my treatment with dates etc. hand-written into it.

There was also information on counselling services, details of who to contact with queries or in an emergency, a list of common questions with their answers, and details of potential complications of treatments such as ovarian hyperstimulation syndrome (OHSS), so that you could recognise this if it happened to you. I'd have been totally lost without this booklet and made sure to have it with me at all times so I could make sure I was taking the correct amount of medication at the correct time.

The first daily medication was called Gonadotropin, which is a stimulation medication containing two hormones, luteinizing hormone (LH) and follicle stimulating hormone (FSH), which are normally produced by the pituitary gland. These hormones stimulate the ovaries to produce a follicle, which contain an egg. It is rare to experience side effects from this ovarian stimulation medication, but occasionally, a mild skin reaction can occur around the injection site, and more commonly, abdominal discomfort will be felt, as the ovaries become stretched by the developing follicles (remembering that you usually only produce one in a cycle, not multiple).

I started taking a high dosage of arnica given to me by a homeopath, which I am sure helped to ease any bruising, and I was very much working on the basis of "there's no reason to feel any side effects, I'm just going to allow my body to do what is required of it by the medication". As I previously mentioned, I just wanted to flow with it all to achieve an outcome, and so life carried on as usual. This isn't to say that I didn't notice some change, only that I wasn't resisting it.

I was still working during this time, although I was fortunate to work flexible part-time hours in an office where I could come and go as I pleased, depending on my workload. I continued to teach yoga and give Reiki to others, as it was a good distraction from the IVF, but I made sure not to overdo it. I was mindful of my energy levels and retreated a little, avoiding situations and people with negative energy so that I could keep my own energy levels as stable and high as possible.

Thus, I embraced the quiet in life with a daily meditation, Yoga Nidra (alternating two Sankalpas, "my eggs are growing and ripening", "I am pregnant with a healthy baby"), and a yoga practice incorporating asana (postures) and pranayama (breathing exercises). I tried to take lots of walks and spend time in nature. I already drank lots of water and ate a healthy diet, but I increased my protein intake. I was also already supplementing with oil of evening primrose, which is known to encourage the development of cell membranes. I still drank the occasional glass of sparkling wine, but was aware that the medication was already taxing my liver, and so I took a supplement of milk thistle tincture daily to support my liver with its processing of the drugs (although some could argue that this was just an additional thing for my liver to process!).

I made an effort to rest as much as I could. I was growing eggs after all and I needed to do all I could to enhance this process. So I invested in the *Downton Abbey* box set and started watching a couple of episodes every evening with a hot water bottle on my tummy (in Chinese medicine, warmth is considered necessary for the development of a baby), before taking a relaxing bath with aromatherapy oils and getting early nights, which was a novelty for me (I had a tendency back then to stay up very late, working on my laptop!). I also received regular acupuncture and reflexology to further relax and ensure my energy was clear. In short, I was visualising healthy eggs, dreaming about healthy eggs, living and breathing healthy eggs. It was absolutely all about the eggs!!

On day seven, I had to start taking an additional daily injection, this time of Cetrotide, which is an antagonist injection. This is used to prevent premature ovulation (early release of eggs from the ovary). This drug rarely causes side effects other than a potential skin irritation around the injection site, although I suspect the arnica helped with this. It was probably around then, however, that I did start to have a little wobble and feel a little bit sorry for myself, what with all the injecting and the hormones now circulating within me.

I could feel self-pity creeping in and in the background: "why me?", "I don't want to be putting these drugs into my body". Then there was the whole underlying stress of it all. I was wondering whether it was working, and felt slight changes, in terms of feeling tired and a little not quite myself, which is hardly surprising, especially when you have spent so long working on being in touch with yourself and your every hormonal change!

Still, I had my motto in my head, "do not give in to self-pity", which was also joined by another motto, "suck it up", which my IVF friend said to me when I started to complain a little to her. It sounds harsh but it works a treat. It's all about the outcome and she was right – self-pity and feeling sorry for myself was not going to help; I literally had to suck it up and get on with it. **If there's one single piece of advice for me to pass on to others from the IVF process, it is this – absolutely no self-pity, suck it up, make a conscious decision to get rid of negative thoughts, stay positive and get on with it.** I will mention this more than once, as I really do believe it's crucial.

On day 10 I attended MSG for blood tests and yet another transvaginal ultrasound scan to see how I had responded to the stimulatory injections. Our consultant, Mr Nzewi, measured the number and size of the follicles, which he recorded and faxed immediately to Wessex. This scan essentially provided an indication of the number of eggs that may have been produced and gave an idea as to the timing for the trigger injection and egg recovery, while the blood tests checked the levels of oestrogen in my blood.

Fortunately, all seemed to have gone well. There is a risk that you produce very few or no follicles, which means that the cycle has to be abandoned. There is also the risk that you produce over 20 follicles (over stimulation), and again, the cycle may have to be abandoned, because to continue could prove a risk to one's health. So, you see, at every stage of the process, there is not only a risk, but also a chance that you may not achieve the outcome, and this can get awfully stressful, especially in the build up to an appointment.

Still, we were doing well, and Wessex told us that I would now need to attend a scan with them at the clinic in Southampton on day 12, which was just two days away. We'd had a feeling that this would be the case, so we were prepared to a point. I had already booked the time off from work and now we could book the ferry ticket. We were planning to take the car with us this time because we would need to be in the UK for a good few days awaiting egg retrieval, and then the time required while the eggs were potentially fertilised by the sperm and grown to either embryos (at three days) or blastocysts (at five days).

We had arranged to stay with one of E's best friends, who was living on his own in a lovely house in Surbiton, at that time. It was only an hour and half drive away from the clinic, which was fine, and meant that we could experience a home-away-from-home environment and could keep our costs down, because ICSI is not cheap. In fact, at that point, February 2013, the treatment, including the initial consultations, screening, testing and now ICSI had cost us £5,885, excluding any travel costs and sundry expenses. This of course merely adds to the stress of it all! So we were very indebted and grateful to our friend for putting us up, free of charge, for the remainder of this treatment cycle.

We took the overnight boat to Portsmouth and I remember feeling rather excited that it was really and truly happening, and that, more importantly, I'd be able to stop with the drugs and the two daily injections. They do begin to get a bit wearing and, little did I realise at the time, it really wasn't for that long, at least in comparison to other IVF treatment schedules. Still, I was hoping that the scan at the clinic would show that we were absolutely good to go and get on with the whole egg retrieval process.

We had a whole other drama going on at this point however. You see, E had put his back out.

He's broken his back twice in the past, so he has a weakness there. But timings being timings, and perhaps not so surprising when you consider the stress of IVF and the pressure on everyone, and on the unsettling and unbalancing nature of it all, his back had gone – well and truly gone. And on the boat over to the UK, his back was causing him quite some pain.

Arriving into Portsmouth at 6a.m., we set out to find somewhere to get breakfast, E hobbling and wincing in pain, before he administered what I hoped would be my final injection, done in the car in an underground car park, feeling rather suspicious and seedy! We had a few hours until my appointment, which would involve yet another transvaginal ultrasound scan for the clinic to determine if my eggs were ready for retrieval, and E was in so much pain, he decided he needed to go to A&E to see someone, as he was worried he wouldn't be able to get through the day!

So off we went to Southampton General A&E, not necessarily ideal when you're already a little on edge about your forthcoming IVF appointment, but needs must. It may have been early in the morning but there was still some queue ahead of E, so after a few hours of waiting around, I had to leave him to it and navigate my way on my own in the car to the appointment and, more importantly, have my first scan on my own!

THE SCAN

Sadly, it seemed it was not our day. The lady who undertook the scan decided that the eggs were not quite ready, they still required a few more days of growing. My heart dropped and I had to really hold back the tears, as I just wanted the injections to be over with, especially as I had to invest in yet more medication at £84 for two days more of injections! One starts to get a little flippant to it all I suppose, and just passes over the debit card, I mean what else can you do?

E was waiting for me by the time I made it back to the hospital, armed with some strong painkillers, and we drove up to Surbiton and settled ourselves into our friend's quiet home. It was Friday, and I left the boys to it as I retreated to our room and watched *Downton Abbey* on my laptop. It became my evening routine. Eat dinner, take a bath and settle down with *Downton Abbey* until it was time to go to sleep! There was no Wi-Fi in his house, and you know, it was a joy really to have a complete break from the world, a proper little retreat.

I complemented my retreating with some yoga. That Saturday, I took myself off to a class with Aram Raffy at TriYoga in Chelsea. I had discovered Aram a few months previously and loved his hard-core vinyasa style of teaching. It was just what I needed; not only do I love nothing more than attending busy yoga classes and practicing with other people, but I love vinyasa yoga and getting out of my head and into my body. As usual, I was buzzing afterwards, and any negativity I may have felt the previous day dissolved during that practice – the joy of yoga!

The same morning, E administered the last Cetrotide antagonist injection, and that evening at 10.30p.m., we had to inject Ovitrelle, which helps to trigger ovulation (the release of the eggs by the ovaries) and the development of a special structure of ovary (the corpus luteum) that helps pregnancy. It was a relief, a joy in fact, to be done with the injections and the pumping myself full of artificial hormones. I mean, I tolerated it as best I could, but there comes a time when you're ready for the next step.

I was fortunate really in that I didn't experience too many side effects, or at least, I didn't allow myself to succumb to them. High levels of oestrogen can cause breast tenderness, headaches, tiredness and vaginal discharge. Also, when the ovaries are distended with follicles, abdominal discomfort may result from the stretching of the wall of the ovary.

I don't know whether it was the acupuncture, or the Reiki, or the yoga, or the arnica, but I didn't feel any pain. Yes, I knew something was going on, but I didn't experience any discomfort as such, just irritation at having to have injections each day! I was incredibly focused on a positive outcome and just did what I was told to achieve that outcome, without thinking too much into it. And here I was, almost there, only another day to go, without any medication (hoorah!) and then we were due at Wessex for egg retrieval.

On the Sunday, I was fortunate to come across a "balancing" workshop with the inspirational Stewart Gilchrist, again at TriYoga in Camden. I took myself up there on the train, leaving E with his friend to potter, and I enjoyed the solitude of being on my own in London and meeting this interesting yoga teacher, who has continued to inspire me ever since. It just felt like it was meant to be, not least because Stewart reminded me a little of Lance Schuler, with whom I undertook my initial yoga teacher training course all those years ago, but because the nature of the packed workshop was on "balance", and I needed all the balancing I could get ahead of egg retrieval the following day.

I most definitely left that session feeling more inspired and balanced in body, mind and soul than when I arrived, and I was excited about what lay ahead. I'd learned some new things, I'd moved my body and practiced a fair few balancing poses, I'd breathed steadily and deeply, and I'd enjoyed the sharing of the focused group energy. In addition, I felt like I had done what I could to energise my eggs with as much oxygen, prana (life force), and light, vibrational energy as possible. I was hoping that those eggs would be shining brightly and would go on to form beautiful embryos, full of life and vitality. I certainly felt like I'd given it my best shot, and now it was just a matter of getting on with the next stage of the procedure.

CHAPTER 5
Egg Retrieval

I was awake early on egg recovery day, due to a combination of excitement and anxiety about the unknown ahead. Plus, our appointment was booked for 10.30a.m., and I wasn't allowed to drink anything beyond 8.30a.m., so I was up in good time to fit in my essential morning cup of tea! That was all I was allowed though, that and water, but nil food by mouth from midnight, so no breakfast for me.

We were also told not to wear perfume, aftershave, hairspray or strong deodorant when attending for egg recovery. Apparently, embryos held within the adjacent laboratory are very sensitive to the chemicals contained in the products, so it's important to avoid using them. I'm all up for the natural approach in any event, but it does make you consider how much these products may affect sensitive hormonal balance and your health generally.

I spent the journey from Surbiton to Wessex, in Southampton, channelling Reiki onto my lower tummy, hoping to infuse the growing eggs with as much loving, healing and energising Reiki energy as possible. I was just really hoping that the eggs were going to be good enough to grow into healthy embryos. It was exciting, certainly, but I was still silently praying that it would all go well – it really is a test of one's ability to stay positive and have faith throughout.

THE RETRIEVAL

I wasn't quite sure what to expect that morning. I'd read the notes in the booklet provided by the clinic, but I was still nervous about what the procedure actually entailed. Fortunately, we only had to wait a few minutes in the waiting area of the clinic before we were led downstairs and into a small consultation room. Here, I was asked to change out of my clothes and into a gown provided by the clinic, before covering myself with my own dressing gown, which I had been asked to bring.

A small cannula was then inserted into my arm. This was probably the most uncomfortable part of the whole procedure, as the nurse had to make a few attempts. Finally, the cannula was in place and before I knew it, I was kissing E goodbye and being led by the nurse across the corridor to the small theatre for the procedure. It was probably a good thing it happened so quickly, as it didn't give me too much time to dwell on what lay ahead.

I was welcomed into the theatre by the consultant and her assisting nurse, both of whom I knew from our previous appointments. I appreciated the continuity of care, although I'm not sure you get that so much these days, with IVF now being so popular. At that time, however, it made a huge difference. It put me at ease, and we were able to chat and joke with some familiarity. The theatre itself wasn't threatening either, as far as I can remember. It just contained a bed with a stool beside it and a large scanning system at the foot of it.

There was a sense of purpose in the room, and after our friendly exchange, I was asked to remove my pants and sit at the base of the treatment bed. It was then that all dignity went well and truly out of the window, as I lay back with my legs padded and strapped up into stirrups. I wasn't expecting this, and it's certainly not an experience I'm in any hurry to repeat. I was soon administered a sedative, which sent me straight to sleep.

I was oblivious to the procedure itself. I'm told that it's not particularly lengthy, perhaps 10-20 minutes; it depends really on how many eggs are being retrieved. The recovery of the eggs from the follicles is generally done using a vaginal ultrasound probe, which guides a needle to aspirate (suck out) each follicle. It's incredible when you think about it, and amazing that science facilitates this.

Once the egg is retrieved, it's studied under a microscope and given a grading, with each clinic having its own grading system. The emphasis is on quality rather than quantity, especially as not all the eggs retrieved will be fertilised, so the number doesn't necessarily give an indication of how many embryos may result. However, to a greater extent, the more eggs the clinic have to work with, the greater the chance of them fertilising, so it's all relevant.

Once the eggs are retrieved, they are put together with the sperm in the laboratory (in-vitro) about four hours after egg retrieval, or, as in our case, the sperm are injected individually into the eggs (ICSI). The eggs are then checked the next morning for evidence of fertilisation. At Wessex, statistics indicate that there's a 5% chance that none of the eggs will achieve fertilisation. This does mean, however, that 95% should be OK!

I remember waking up in the recovery room and being surprised to find that it was all over. It felt like it had been seconds since I lay down on the bed in the theatre. The number of other ladies in the room also amazed me, as I had been unaware of them upon arrival at the clinic. There was a lady in the bed next to me, and I could hear a couple of other ladies chatting beyond the thin curtain that separated us – the nurse confirmed that it was indeed a busy morning.

I was very excited that there was full moon due later that evening. Not only do I literally worship the Goddess of the Moon, but she is also the Goddess of Fertility, and the full moon is a time when women are (in theory) most fertile. When I first learnt about the lunar cycle, I found it fascinating that despite us all taking fertility drugs, our "cycles" were somehow still connected to the moon. Whether we are aware of it or not, as women, our bodies are connected to, and influenced by, the moon's energies (it's certainly sub-conscious, if not conscious). The feminine qualities of the moon are highly celebrated with many moon goddesses linked to "her". The Great Goddess worshipped in old Europe became equated with the moon, in whose divine light she was reflected. As the moon waxed and waned, so did the inherent power of the Goddess. The timing was a very good sign indeed. I was jubilant at the auspicious nature of the timing with my eggs being fertilised within the energy of a fertile full moon!

I was keen to share my excitement about the full moon IVF gathering with whoever would listen. The poor lady in the bed beside me couldn't avoid my ramblings and I was delighted to educate her about the connection between the full moon and fertility, and the auspicious timing of us both having our eggs retrieved on this day. She told me that this was her third attempt at IVF; the first two cycles had failed. I can't imagine what that must have felt like, and I hoped that the moon would work some magic for her too. Unfortunately, I shall never know whether she conceived, but I like to think she did.

The nurses were less interested in my moon tales. I don't think they really understood the significance; it was just another day for them. There was a time when I too didn't really know much about the moon, and I certainly didn't understand or recognise the correlation between the moon cycle and my own cycle. Nor did I appreciate the power of the menstrual cycle as it moves us from girl to woman, through to wise woman and on to crone; it was just something that happened every month.

Further, I had no idea of the way in which we can use our menstrual cycle to connect with our innate feminine wisdom – the wisdom of our grandmothers and great grandmothers, and all the wise women that have lived before us – and the fact that this is available to us all the time. It's something that every woman should be taught when she first begins menstruating, because it offers us so much insight into how we are living our lives, and can be deeply empowering – imperative for any lady with menstrual issues.

Since I discovered the wonders of the Goddess of Moon, I have been honouring her, praying to her and dancing with her whenever I can – quite literally too. There is nothing quite as uplifting or likely to make you feel wired and buzzing as dancing naked in the light of a full moon. I highly recommend it to anyone who wants to deepen their connection to her, and feel her energy, especially anyone with fertility issues. If that's not your bag then just stand under her light with your arms held high and be moon touched instead.

But be prepared, she likes to shake things up a little in her quest to bring out the light in you (so that you may shine as brightly as she does when full). She'll ask you to dance with her and shake yourself loose, surrendering to the moment and all that it holds for you. She's a blessing and brings blessings with her too. I was excited about her appearing on egg retrieval day – it was as though my prayers had been answered, which strengthened my faith in the magic of the Universe.

Recovery

After an hour sitting in one of the armchairs in the recovery room, drinking tea and literally recovering from the procedure, I was allowed to leave. It really was that simple, although the clinic insists that someone collects you, as you are still recovering from the sedative. I changed back into my clothes and E came down to collect me. It was then that our kind nurse met us and told us that they had retrieved 11 eggs during the procedure, and that these were now with the embryologists for grading.

She told us to return in three days' time for embryo transfer, and that was that. It was exciting but I was very aware that the eggs might not fertilise or indeed be of a fertilising quality that would allow for embryo transfer. IVF really is a waiting game, from one procedure to the next. It can get so exhausting just waiting to hear the results of the various tests and procedures, and never being quite certain if you'll be able to move on to the next stage or not.

Still, I was feeling positive – the moon was full and I was quite sure her energy would work some magic and help to fertilise the eggs. Plus, I was rather hyper from the combined effects of the sedative and the relief of getting through egg retrieval. This meant I talked non-stop to E all the way back to Surbiton. It was like being giddy from a glass of champagne – I'd like to bottle that feeling! Poor E was also relieved that the procedure was over and was looking forward to a few days of lying on the sofa and resting his back, which was still very painful.

The clinic advise you to do very little, certainly no driving, no alcohol and no signing of legal documentation, in the 24 hours following egg retrieval. They mention that you may experience some discomfort following the procedure, with a swollen and sore abdomen and some cramping that may require strong painkillers. They also advise you to abstain from sexual intercourse until you have received the result of the pregnancy test, as the ovaries may remain enlarged and intercourse can potentially damage them. In addition, some eggs may remain uncollected and these could potentially give rise to significant multiple pregnancy.

For me, between now and embryo transfer, it was absolutely all about healing from egg retrieval and preparing my uterus to receive the fertilised embryo(s). I saw it as a mission and set to work as soon as I got in the car, taking some high dosage arnica and channelling Reiki into my lower tummy. Back at the house in Surbiton, I continued with the Reiki while nestled up in bed with a hot water bottle on my abdomen. I like a good mission and I like healing work, so I was looking forward to seeing how I could heal myself within this short time period.

Chapter 6

Preparing for Embryo Transfer

Egg retrieval brings risks. It's common to experience some bowel disturbance such as constipation or diarrhoea following the operation. Sometimes, there can be some vaginal bleeding and, in rare cases, OHSS. OHSS is a serious condition, which can cause: abdominal swelling and pain, shortness of breath, feeling faint and reduced urine output.

OHSS usually occurs several days after egg collection when the ovarian cysts fill with fluid and the fluid collects in the abdomen. In severe cases, the fluid also collects around the lungs. OHSS sometimes requires admission to hospital to ensure adequate hydration and to treat the pain, so needs to be taken very seriously. It's certainly one of those things to look out for.

Fortunately, I was lucky, as I didn't experience OHSS or vaginal bleeding. I also did what I could to support my digestive system, by eating plenty of vegetables, brown rice and flax seeds, drinking plenty of water, taking probiotics and giving myself Reiki. The ancient yogis say that "dis-ease" originates in the digestive system, and I certainly feel out of sorts if my digestive system is challenged in any way, so supporting it throughout IVF generally is essential.

I also took extra Vitamin C to help with the healing and of course arnica, which I have come to recognise as nothing short of a miracle plant. You can take arnica in tablet form but you can apply the cream to your lower tummy too. I also took milk thistle to support my liver, from the effects of the sedative from egg retrieval.

Reiki, Yoga & Chinese Medicine

Back at our friend's house in Surbiton, I was determined to focus on healing myself and preparing for the next stage of the treatment. I wanted my body to be as healthy and clean as possible, my chakras balanced and glowing, and my energy channels to be clear – mind, body and soul perfectly aligned! I also wanted my womb to be warm, cosy and inviting, so that any new life would choose to grow in there.

I enjoy a mission, especially a healing one, and tried to listen to my body, do what it needed, and get myself as prepared as possible for embryo transfer. This meant that during that first afternoon and evening, I rested in bed, placing a hot water bottle on my tummy to bring healing heat to my womb, and channelling Reiki into myself too. Reiki was key for me, and the next morning, I had arranged a Reiki session at a holistic centre in a nearby town.

The treatment was with a mother and daughter team, so that meant four hands on me and double the amount of Reiki than one would receive from just one practitioner. It was amazing! None of us had ever experienced such heat during a treatment. The ladies' hands were burning and they had to remove their jumpers to cope with the heat they were feeling. After a while, I dropped deeply into a state of relaxation.

It was an incredible experience – I've channelled and received a lot of Reiki in my time, but this session was powerful indeed. There was no doubt that my body absolutely wanted to heal, and it was absorbing as much Reiki energy as it could during the time available to it. To this day, I still marvel at the magic of Reiki and the manner in which it heals. I felt calm, "whole" and grounded after the session, like I'd come back to Earth a little.

I shared with the ladies the reason that I was visiting them, and it caught me a little, because the daughter was terribly sympathetic and asked me how many attempts we had had with the IVF. When I responded that this was our first, she was even more sympathetic, and wished me good luck. It was a very different reaction to how I was feeling in my head, as I had no doubt at that point that all would be well, and it caught me off hand a little. She was incredibly well-meaning, but I didn't want sympathy.

It reminded me of the need to retreat during this precious time and maintain my grounding and faith in the process. However well-meaning people intend to be, this is a period of intense vulnerability, and it is essential not to fall into the victim mentality. As I have mentioned before, pity has no place in IVF. Nor any comments that may be construed as negative. One must gently withdraw into one's own place and listen to the inner guidance about how to support the process. Lesson learned!

That late afternoon I took myself off to a Bikram yoga class. Bikram is not really my thing, but E's best friend likes to attend, so I always accompany him when we are staying in Surbiton. It's yoga in a heated room, practiced in front of a mirror, and follows the same sequence in each class. There are 26 poses, which are chosen to "*systematically move fresh, oxygenated blood to one hundred percent of your body, to each organ and fibre, restoring all systems to healthy working order, just as nature intended*" (www.bikramyoga.com).

I struggle a little with the heat; it's pretty intense, like being in a sauna. And I don't particularly enjoy practicing in front of a mirror. Plus, I find the sequencing challenging as it's static and you practice each pose twice. But, despite all of this, it does make you feel very clean, as you sweat so profusely throughout the class, and it can be really energising too. I always leave on a high and feel incredibly stretched the next day.

In this instance, I had a feeling that Bikram might assist with my healing process and help to bring fresh blood to my uterus. I also felt that it would help to quieten my mind and promote a positive mental state – if nothing else, it would be a distraction and time filler! It was the first time I had been to one of these classes on my own, and I was surprised how much I enjoyed it. Not only was it fabulous to be anonymous, but I was able to drop into my body without any one distracting me. It was certainly what I needed.

The next morning, I attended a different yoga class at a lady's house a five-minute drive from where we were staying. It's not the first time I've come across this in the outer London area, where a female yoga teacher turns a room in her house into a yoga studio, accommodating six to eight students at a time, creating a real community feel. The practice was great too; there's much benefit from practicing in the company, and indeed energy, of other women.

After the class, I visited a dear friend who lived near London. She had gone through IVF a few years before me and was a wealth of knowledge and experience, and it made a huge difference to me to be able to talk to someone who had already been through IVF. She was an incredible support to me during this time, for which I shall always be grateful. I would certainly encourage anyone going through IVF to find a positive IVF friend to confide in, as it does make such a difference.

My friend had conceived through her first IVF attempt, also with ICSI, and this heartened me. I was also encouraged by the fact that we had both had the same number of eggs collected at egg retrieval, and I hoped mine would fertilise as well as hers had done. She still had some embryos in storage, which could be used at a future attempt, and this was certainly my ideal outcome. It was lovely to chat things through and leave feeling incredibly positive about our chances of conceiving too.

Later that afternoon, E and I pottered around Richmond Park. We both felt the need for fresh air and nature. I don't think you can ever underestimate the positive effect that nature has on the soul. It helps to make you feel more connected to something greater than yourself, and there can be much comfort in this. It was refreshing to feel the soft earth beneath our feet and to marvel at the deer, while breathing the fresh and cool winter air.

We were due back to Wessex the next day for embryo transfer. E's back was feeling the stress of this, as he struggled to find a comfortable position, and was taking painkillers continuously. It was fascinating for me to witness the manner in which his mental stress manifested physically – his root chakra was feeling the strain. This was new territory for both of us and we were both feeling a little shaky in our own ways.

By day 3, I was certainly beginning to feel the strain. While no news was certainly good news, I desperately wanted the clinic to call me and tell me that we had a sufficient number of potential quality embryos (day 3) for them to be able to progress a couple through to the blastocyst stage (day 6). This would give the embryologists more time to study the developing embryo and determine whether it was more likely to develop into a healthy pregnancy.

By the evening, we had not received a call, so we carried on life as usual, with another early night watching *Downton Abbey* and yet more channelling of Reiki into my tummy. It was a restless night of trying to sleep. I was now beginning to feel the stress a little more than I had done previously. It was all very real. I was desperate to hear from the clinic, desperate for some reassurance, but also aware that they would only call when necessary. It was one big waiting game again.

The next morning (day 4), I was very much on edge. Wessex still hadn't called, so we left Surbiton about 9a.m. to drive down to the clinic in time for our appointment. This didn't feel right though, and after driving for about 10 minutes, E pulled over, parked the car and called the clinic to double check that the embryo transfer would definitely be taking place. The receptionist took a message and advised him that one of the embryologists would call us back, so we continued with our journey, me now feeling super on edge awaiting the call.

Fortunately, the call arrived quickly and I spoke to the embryologist directly. He told me that they had cultured eight embryos. Five were developing well so of these five the best three were taken to blastocyst and the best two after the initial three for blastocyst were frozen as embryos. The remaining three (of the eight) were not of good enough quality for them to use in the IVF process and did not develop any further. This was amazingly good news. I could have jumped with joy. *Phew, what a relief!* It was exactly what I wanted to hear. I had been visualising and praying for two healthy blastocysts and we were one step closer to realising this.

E turned the car around and we headed back to Surbiton, safe in the knowledge that all being well, we wouldn't need to return for a further three days, which gave me an extra two full days to prepare my body for the transfer. I intended to make the most of this. I attended two more Bikram yoga classes and started to get really into it, which surprised me! I also listened to a number of Yoga Nidras. I am a great believer that the innate intelligence of the mind-body takes from this practice what it needs, and I needed a combination of deep rest and creative stimulus – I was creating new life after all.

I continued to eat a good diet containing lots of brown rice, fruits and vegetables during this time. I also continued to enjoy a glass of sparkling wine each evening while cooking dinner (although I didn't have one the evening prior to embryo transfer, as it didn't feel right for me). There are no rules about this though, and I read about a consultant who positively encouraged women to enjoy a daily glass of wine during IVF, especially after embryo transfer, to relax and reduce their stress levels.

I was also keen to nourish my soul and cleanse my aura with nature, and while I certainly missed being able to swim in the sea, or just being on a beach, we made the most of the nature available to us. Thus, we tried to spend as much time as we could outside those few days, treading the earth, breathing fresh air and hugging trees – never underestimate the power of this; there is much energy, support and joy that comes from connecting with Mother Earth like this!

We were also fortunate to have access to Chinese medicine in Surbiton. We both had acupuncture, and while it seemed to make little difference to E's back pain, I certainly felt the benefit as it left me feeling particularly energised. I also received some reflexology, and the lovely Chinese doctor, on hearing I was preparing for embryo transfer, spent more time with me than she was meant to – my life was blessed with many healing angels during this period.

Admittedly, all these extra treatments cost money, but by this point, we were done with worrying about the financial aspect. It was our first attempt after all, and I was keen to do what I could holistically to support the treatment. I was mindful, however, of only working with people who felt aligned. I was aware – and continue to be aware – of how fertility has become big business, with people profiteering from women's (often desperate) need to conceive.

There are now a multitude of supplements and other products available that are marketed specifically at fertility. There is also a multitude of people offering their services to help you conceive, whether through holistic treatments or coaching. While this all has a place, it's essential not to give your power away to others during this time and believe that they know you better than you know yourself. They don't. They can't!

Like with anything in life, it's only you who can really make it happen, and retaining self-belief, self-worth and a sense of hope are essential – anything that takes this away from you needs to be avoided. Thus, you mustn't just do something because someone else tells you to, or because it worked for them. You do it because it feels right for you, and not from a place or attitude of desperation.

I tried to stay as empowered and true to myself as possible. Thus, by the time embryo transfer day arrived, I felt that I had done all I could do, in the time available to me, to prepare myself physically, mentally, emotionally, and indeed spiritually, to receive new life. I was a little anxious about the procedure, as it was still an unknown to me, but I was delighted that we had finally gotten to this part of the process. I was feeling hopeful and excited, and keen to get on with the next stage of our journey...

Chapter 7

Embryo Transfer

Embryo transfer – or in this case, blastocyst transfer – was due to take place late morning on a wintry Saturday, in early March 2013. In many respects, it was perfect timing. I'm a Pagan at heart, and we were a month away from having celebrated Imbolc, which, in the Celtic seasonal calendar, marks the beginning of the lambing season and signals the initial start of spring and the stirrings of new life – the reawakening of the earth.

The underlying energy of this time is explained by the meaning of the original word "Imbolg", which means "in the belly". All is pregnant and expectant – and only just visible if at all – like the gentle curve of a "just-showing" pregnancy. It brings with it the promise of renewal, of hidden potential, of earth awakening and life-force stirring. There is hope and light at the end of the tunnel. It is a time to celebrate the returning light and witness life's insatiable appetite for rebirth.

This is a time to let go of the past and look to the future, clearing out the old, and making both outer and inner space for new beginnings. It's a good time for spring cleaning and wish-making. It's also a good time to prepare for what you wish to accomplish in the months ahead. At this time, you will want to clarify and refine what you began to work on at Yule, the winter solstice.

Imbolc is also a time for celebrating the Celtic Goddess, Brigid. Brigid is the Goddess of poetry, healing, smithcraft and midwifery. She is the Goddess of fire, of the sun and of the hearth. She brings fertility to the land and its people, and is closely connected to midwives and newborn babies. She is the triple Goddess (maiden, mother and crone), but at Imbolc, she is in her maiden and virgin aspect.

Therefore, it was appropriate timing. I was a maiden wanting to become a mother; ripe with new potential and the stirrings of new-life force. I had begun the journey some time ago, but made my intentions very clear at Yule. The dream of pregnancy was now becoming more of a reality, and it felt like nature was supporting this with her spring energy. On some level, unconscious, though I had been aware of it, it was indeed perfect timing for new beginnings!

The transfer

We were the only patients in the clinic that morning, which made the clinic feel less clinical somehow; more relaxed and personal. It helped that we knew both the consultant and nurse too. They were the ones whom we had initially met in Guernsey, and who had been with us at our initial appointment in the clinic in January, the consultant having delivered the good news that we could begin ICSI. The familiarity felt special.

It still makes me laugh to reflect on how events unfolded. Initially, at the time E and I first talked about having a baby, I prayed for a very conscious conception. And now, here we were, experiencing exactly that. Admittedly, it was absolutely not in the manner I had imagined, but a conscious moment nonetheless.

It's a good reminder that we must be careful what we wish for, and to let go of any expectation of how our wish may manifest, as it is rarely in the manner we anticipate. So here we found ourselves, in a very clinical environment in Southampton, with monitors and scanners, and a consultant and a nurse. It certainly wasn't the stuff of dreams, and I was aware that I was going to have to dig deep to find the spiritual in all this.

Still, one does what one can, and the clinic being less-clinic-like than it would be ordinarily (there being no other patients or members of staff rushing around) helped enormously, as well as the fact that we had already established a friendly relationship with the consultant and nurse. For me especially, this relationship meant a lot, and I feel very strongly that having a relationship like this with the staff helps enormously with the whole IVF process, and certainly with embryo transfer.

It felt that we had luck on our side, and there was a light-hearted energy in the air; the Divine was supporting us, I had no doubt. I felt positive, excited and upbeat about what lay ahead, and the only thing really troubling me in that moment was my bladder, which had to be half-full in preparation for the procedure. The clinic tells you how much water to drink and when, but it felt like my bladder was bursting, rather than just the half-full intended!

Fortunately, the appointment was running to schedule and everything happened very quickly after we arrived. The nurse led us from the reception (where I was busily channelling Reiki onto my tummy and trying to ignore my bladder's call for the toilet) down the stairs to the theatre room, where I had to remove my fluffy boots and leave them by the door, whilst E had to put what looked like blue plastic bags over his shoes.

We were then led into the theatre room, where the consultant was busying herself. E was directed to the stool beside the bed and me to the bed itself, as the embryologist joined us from the adjoining laboratory. The embryologist asked me to confirm my name to ensure that the blastocysts that were being prepared for transfer were mine. This was certainly not a time for making mistakes, and I was grateful for the security, even if it did feel a little silly having to confirm who I was.

She then showed us pictures of different quality blastocysts and explained that we had produced three very good quality grade blastocysts (as previously mentioned, the other two embryos from the five chosen for the IVF process had been frozen). *Wow, I could have jumped with joy! What a relief.* We couldn't have hoped for a better outcome that morning. And it was in that moment that I knew all would be well. Any doubt I may have had disappeared.

The embryologist advised that she had selected two of the blastocysts for transfer, with the other remaining blastocyst being frozen for a future cycle (if we chose). It was strange. As the embryologist explained this to us, I just had this all-consuming feeling, a sense then, that that one remaining blastocyst would be very important to us one day. While I had certainly never intended to have three children, I also knew that there was no way I would be able to just let that blastocyst be put to waste.

It was a situation I had discussed with my IVF friend – the dilemma of what to do with any extra embryos that you may be lucky enough to create. It's a wonderful position to find yourself in, when others have such difficulty in producing one quality embryo, let alone have a surplus like us. But it can create a dilemma, because there's potential new life in the embryos, and it's very difficult to just turn your back on that and let it go down the drain.

It was soon time for the transfer. While the embryologist returned to the laboratory to prepare the two chosen blastocysts, I was directed to a small changing cubicle at the side of the room to remove my tights and pants. From there, I was directed onto the bed and had to shuffle down to its end so that my legs could be placed up into the dreaded stirrups again. E was positioned beside me on his stool.

As we waited for the embryologist to return, the lovely consultant took the opportunity to remind me what I should or shouldn't be doing while we waited the 12 days until we could take a pregnancy test. It was a little surreal hearing her talking about pregnancy tests, and especially that I might find myself pregnant in 12 days' time – it was really happening! Here we were, awaiting embryo transfer, which may well lead to pregnancy. Oh my gosh!

She reminded me to take the luteal support, which I had started taking a few days earlier in preparation for implantation, and indeed pregnancy. This is progesterone, a hormone that helps to prepare the uterine lining to accept a fertilised egg, and provide support for a developing embryo. It's administered by way of a pessary, Cyclogest, which has to be inserted into the vagina morning and evening. Sore breasts and feeling emotional are the potential side effects.

The consultant mentioned a chance of some blood spotting and "period type" pains following embryo transfer, and that one can feel a little bloated too. She also explained to me that the embryos couldn't become dislodged in the uterus, as they are held between the walls of the uterus, where surface tension forces are far greater than gravity. I was reassured by this because, silly as it may sound, it had crossed my mind, and of course, I didn't want to do anything unintentionally that may compromise the potential pregnancy.

The consultant also advised that there is no current evidence to suggest that full and complete rest for the 12 days following transfer will improve the chances of a successful pregnancy. However, she did stress the fact that, psychologically, it is important a woman feels that she has done everything possible to promote potential implantation.

I was advised to avoid strenuous exercise, hot baths or saunas that raise your core body temperature, sexual intercourse, ibuprofen, smoky environments, and drinking more than three caffeinated drinks a day. Other than that, it was life as normal, and I certainly intended to get back into the swing of things when I got home. I've never been one for sitting around, and with 12 days to wait to take the test, I knew that I would need to keep busy; that's just my way!

The embryologist returned to the room and I re-confirmed my name to her, feeling particularly silly about doing so a second time! The consultant then set about inserting a small flexile catheter into my vagina, up through the cervical canal and into the uterus. We could see this all happening on the screen positioned at the end of the bed, the nurse sliding the ultrasound device over my lower tummy to get the clearest view.

As I had been told to expect, the sensation is similar to having a smear test, which means it wasn't painful as such, more so uncomfortable. This discomfort is a result of the combination of the fact your legs are in stirrups; there's pressure on your bladder and your cervix is making itself known to you. I gripped E's hand and focused on my breath, practicing the Ujaii breath, in and out, deepening the inhalation and lengthening the exhalation.

The consultant found what she believed to be the optimal position and before we knew it, a star flashed up on the screen as she released the teeny, tiny blastocysts inside me. It was an amazing sight, just as my IVF friend had said it would be. I'm so pleased she told me to look out for this, as it disappears quickly. It's a moment I shall never forget, that star, the flash of life, all parts coming together, the essence of spirit, conception, truly magical to be a witness to this.

Here's another piece of advice for anyone going through IVF. Look out for that star. It's a blessing to be able to witness the vibrancy of life like this. We were fortunate in that the moment was captured on paper, so we have a record of it today, and we both still talk about it to this day.

The catheter was slowly removed and the embryologist was called back into the room to take it back to the lab, to check that both blastocysts had indeed been released. This only took a short moment before she was able to confirm that yes, they'd both been released. With that, my legs were removed from the stirrups and I was helped off the bed and guided back to the changing area to put my pants and tights back on again, before relieving my bladder.

That was that. It was certainly not the stuff of dreams and it was absolutely not the environment I had in mind for the conscious conception either. Nope, this was as clinical as you could get, quite literally in a clinic, and with others watching on too. Still, here's the thing: it *was* incredibly conscious because both E and I were incredibly, totally, utterly, absolutely aware, mindful, present, and all those other words that mean you are very conscious of that exact moment.

In truth, if there's one thing IVF brings you, it's awareness of the process of conception. How can you be anything but aware with all the appointments and scans, the drugs and examinations, and everything having an exact timing to it? You feel every single step of the journey from beginning to end. Your nerves are tested time and time again. There's certainly no drunken "Wham, bam, thank you ma'am" moments with IVF!

There's also no certainty with IVF, and both the nurse and the consultant wished us luck as we left the clinic. Back in the car, we sat quietly for a moment, letting it all sink in. I couldn't stop smiling. It felt a little like a whirlwind, but here we were, procedure completed. I felt this overwhelming desire to give thanks.

So we drove straight to Salisbury, which has since become something of a place of pilgrimage for us. On the way, I started channelling Reiki on my lower tummy, just below the navel, and suddenly realised that I could feel the energy of the blastocysts inside me. It was truly incredible, an energy I had never felt previously, and this both fascinated and overwhelmed me.

It's difficult to put it into words, but I have since come to recognise that it was the igniting energy of pure spirit. It is like the initial spark of a lighter or the initial flame of a candle. It is the momentary pause between an exhalation and an inhalation, the bit that causes the inhalation to arise again. It is the energy of Imbolc, full of new beginnings and potential new life. The truth is, it is the lightest and most expansive energy I have ever felt.

It's so new and alive and vibrant, so much so that I cannot liken it to anything else. Perhaps if I had to try, I would say that it's a little like bottling up the energy at the very beginning of spring – and here we were, at the very beginning of spring too. There is magic in all life. Frequently, we are too busy or too distracted to notice it. Here, I felt privileged and blessed to have the capacity to feel such magic within me. It's pure, unconditional love, essentially.

I am repeatedly awestruck by the beauty of Salisbury Cathedral. It pulls me in. There is something about its ancient energy that finds me gravitating to its walls, hands held against the cool stone. I do this regularly in churches and places of worship. You can feel the love in the structure of the building, and I wanted to infuse and bathe my body and my soul in this beautiful energy, so that the blastocysts would know they had come home.

I sat on my own at the very front of the cathedral, staring up into the stained glass windows and losing myself in all they represent. I'm not religious, but in that moment, my faith was stronger than it had ever been. Surprisingly, going through IVF had strengthened this. I felt like we had been supported and guided the whole way. Now, I just had to maintain this faith and trust in the outcome, whatever that may be.

For now, it was about doing what I felt to do to support the new life growing inside me. I prayed for guidance and gave thanks. I thanked and thanked and thanked. I now knew that I was about to be tested, not only in faith and trust, but also in patience.

Chapter 8

The Pregnancy Test Waiting Game

The limited boat schedule meant that we had to spend an additional 48 hours in the UK following embryo transfer. This was a blessing in many respects, as it prevented me from rushing around, as I have a tendency to do, at home. Resting has never come easily to me, embryo transfer or not. However, it wasn't quite the uneventful and restful time we had anticipated.

The day following embryo transfer, we pottered around the South Downs, visiting Stansted House, which is a Grade II listed Edwardian country house, set on a 1,750-acre estate within the South Downs National Trust. It is well worth a visit if you happen to be in the area. It has a fabulous arboretum, which was a delight for E, not least, because he's a tree surgeon with a passion for trees, but because it distracted him from the increasing pain in his back.

From there, we drove to Petworth Park, which is host to incredible gardens, designed by Lancelot Capability Brown. I studied Capability Brown at university, so it was a big deal for me to see his work first hand. Capability Brown is reputed as the super-guru of parkland landscaping. He was hired at Petworth in 1751, and it is said that he left hardly a square foot of the gardens untouched. It's amazing!

We had a wonderful day together and I was expecting us to return to the hotel for dinner that evening before lazing around on the bed, watching TV – a treat, as I would soon be teaching yoga again most evenings. However, E had other ideas. The pain in his back was acute and he was now experiencing shooting pains down his left leg. He became increasingly anxious and felt he needed to see a doctor.

THE STRESS ON E

So it followed that my imagined restful TV night remained exactly that – imagined! Instead, I found myself driving E to Southampton on the M27 at speed, in the dark, and with rain pelting on the windscreen. Not fun! And to be honest, we were silly really because we were staying just up the road from Portsmouth, but E thought it better to return to Southampton, as he had already visited their A&E department at the beginning of the trip. Big mistake!

It was Sunday early evening after all, and while we'll never know if Portsmouth would have been any better, Southampton A&E department was jam-packed. I've never known anything like it; we're certainly spoilt in Guernsey. Triage "prioritised" E to the bottom of the list, which was positive on the one hand, but did mean a long wait for us on very uncomfortable plastic seats. This was not quite the relaxing evening I had in mind.

By 8p.m., I was anxious for food. The clinic encourages healthy eating for successful implantation, and here I was, stuck in an A&E department with only a snack machine at my disposal, or a fast-food establishment in the main hospital itself (get that, fast food in a hospital!). This left me with little choice but to head out on my own in the car to try and find something to eat, and then try and navigate my way back to the hospital successfully again.

I managed it though, finding a Co-op and buying myself a pre-packaged salad, which I ate in the car. It wasn't ideal and I felt a little sorry for myself. This was not what I had in mind for adequately feeding the little embryos hopefully growing inside me! Still, one does what one needs to do, and I had never seen E in quite so much pain. Fortunately, by the time I returned, E had moved from the waiting room into the A&E treatment area.

It wasn't until 10.30p.m., however, that E was finally seen by a doctor. The doctor carried out the usual tests to determine that there was no apparent nerve damage, before sending E on his way with a prescription for drugs he already had. While it felt a little like a wasted journey, at least E was reassured that there was nothing massively serious going on and he could carry on life as normal, at least until we got home and he could see his own GP.

Being a holistic therapist, it was absolutely no surprise to me that E's back had deteriorated whilst we had been undertaking the IVF. As a potentially older first time dad, and one who had, until a few years earlier, been very non-committal about, well, commitment really, it was inevitable that this life changing and committed event would unground him and test his roots.

In addition, E's back is where he carries his stress, and if ever there was a stressful time to be had then IVF is up there. It's easy to overlook the stress that partners go through during IVF. While it may be us women going through the injecting and the scans, the egg recovery and embryo transfer, the men are going through their own process too. They often feel at a loss to know how to help, especially if the need for IVF is due to male fertility issues. It's a testing time for everyone.

Leaving the hospital late that evening, I was initially irritated with E for getting himself so worked up about the IVF and his back pain. I felt like he was stealing my thunder, which is a terrible thing to say, but I was supposed to be resting and looking after myself in that critical 48 hour-period. Instead, here I was, driving us both back to our hotel at 11p.m. in the pitch black and the continuous rain, when I should have been tucked up in bed.

I came around to seeing the funny side and we still joke about it this day; how he couldn't cope with it being all about me and made sure it was now all about him instead! It certainly was all about him those next few days because he continued to be in huge amounts of pain. It didn't help that we had to endure a seven-hour ferry return crossing to

Guernsey the next day. For me, however, it was ideal, as I got to rest and channel lots of Reiki onto my lower tummy.

THE WAITING GAME

It felt a little strange arriving back in Guernsey that Monday afternoon. We had gone away the two of us, yet, here we were – in theory – returning four of us instead. Everything looked the same, yet, we had changed. Our relationship had deepened – how could it not? But it was more than that. Without having to say anything to each other, we both knew that life would never be the same again, regardless of whether the IVF worked.

I was still feeling confident of success, but the fact we still had to wait 10 days to take a pregnancy test was unnerving. Waiting does not come easily to me. I've always had a tendency towards impatience, which has frequently been tested these past few years. I doubt that there has ever been a single lady going through IVF who has felt calm, collected and patient during this 12 to 14-day period (12 days for blastocysts, 14 days for embryos).

I tried to keep busy so that the time would pass quickly. I returned to working in the office and teaching yoga again. I offered Reiki treatments too. No one would have known what we had just been through; it was very much life as usual to the outside world. Inside, however, I was doing what I could to hold it together, dropping deeply into my spiritual practice to try to keep my faith and spirit high during this decidedly edgy time.

I was fortunate in that I could feel the new life growing inside me, which helped enormously. As someone who works with energy, it was incredibly exciting to feel such vibrant and pure energy, the spark of new life. As the days went on, the energy changed, and it began to feel like running your hands over a string of pearls. It's like the energy becomes a little more contained, a little heavier, but with movement, a circular movement, as they grow inside.

I really wish every lady who undertakes IVF could feel the energy of the embryo(s), not least because it is like nothing else, but because at least you know then that the embryo is still alive and growing inside you, and this can give you so much comfort. It really is such a horrible time, especially if you have suffered a failed cycle previously.

For us, this was our first time, and we had no reason to doubt the process. We had done what was asked of us and deep down, I had this unwavering faith that it was all going to be OK. It wasn't until a few years later that I discovered what it feels like when you don't have this faith – it makes for an extremely stressful and anxious wait, at a time when you should be keeping your stress and anxiety levels to a minimum.

That's not to say that during this time, there weren't moments of doubt and fear. The mind is tricky like that. Fear I find particularly fascinating, as it feels so real and yet, it is not real at all. It translates as "False Evidence Appearing Real", and if you can remind yourself of this when you feel it taking hold then it helps enormously in recognising it for what it is and letting it go. It's not easy though.

I've no doubt that my daily meditation practice helped enormously in keeping my mind strong and focused during this time. I would wholeheartedly encourage any lady going through IVF to carve out some time in your day to just sit in silent meditation and be with whatever comes up for you. Do not try to change it or turn away from it, but just sit with the emotion or feeling, whatever it may be.

I would sit in Siddhasana (the accomplished pose), which is a comfortable seated pose for me, making sure that my knees were lower than my hips, so that I could sit with ease and with a tall spine. You could kneel or sit on a chair though if that is more comfortable for you and means that you are less distracted by discomfort in the physical body (some people find sitting cross-legged desperately uncomfortable on their knees, hips and back).

Once I had settled myself, I would then drop my awareness into my body and just notice what was going on in there.

More often than not in that pregnancy-test-waiting-period, I'd find some unease right down in the pit of my stomach, perhaps a little fear, or doubt or anxiety, that uncomfortable and edgy feeling that can bring with it butterflies and nausea, and make you want to turn away from it.

However, if you sit with it, so keep the awareness on the sensation, however challenging that is, the less awkward and edgy it feels. It is even better if you can lift that sensation from the tummy into the heart, so from the tummy, bring the awareness up into the heart and settle the attention there instead. I always find the heart a reassuring place to hold awareness, as it is the seat of love and compassion and here, the rhythm of the heart beat (if you truly drop into that space) can be a source of much comfort.

Even just five minutes can make a huge difference to centre and check in daily. It is in this way that you come to recognise the illusion that is fear and the manner in which you're mind works and the negative thinking that can arise during the IVF process.

During this waiting period, I also continued to practice yoga and Yoga Nidra daily, and I did a huge amount of praying and talking to the angels. I love the angels and make no apology for this. Since they've been in my life, they have provided much comfort and guidance. I certainly felt their presence during this time, which helped to buoy my spirits. I regularly read my angel cards and during this period, the "child" and "new beginnings" cards kept flying out, which certainly helped!

I also noticed white feathers in front of my path, which are a sign that the angels are surrounding you and that all is well – there is a Divine Plan to all life! I noticed robins during this period too. They are believed to be another sign that the angels are with you and that it is time to sing your own song for a new period in your life. They will also teach you how to incorporate new beginnings with faith and trust in the process, which seemed incredibly appropriate.

I was channelling still Reiki into my tummy at every available opportunity, sometimes below the navel to nourish my uterus and the growing blastocysts, but also above the navel to support my digestive system (said to be the seat of all illness by ancient Yogis), and help to ease any anxiety or fear arising in this area of the body, which is sometimes referred to as the navel centre or the solar plexus. Sometimes, I would have a hand on both, or alternate as I felt appropriate – I also wish every lady going through IVF could be Reiki attuned to be able to do this.

I enjoyed going for Reiki treatments too. I was keen to do all I could to ground and balance my energy. I walked and swam as often as I could, but avoided strenuous activity, like netball, which I had been playing prior to IVF. I also kept a low profile socially and retreated as best I could.

E was very much forced to retreat during this time as his back had become so bad that he spent his days between the sofa or floor, drugged up on very strong painkillers and trying to lie flat. He had been to see his GP and was awaiting a referral to see a surgeon in Exeter. It was tough for him; he wasn't able to distract himself from the impending pregnancy test, other than by watching an awful lot of *Miami Vice*!

As I mentioned earlier, I was increasingly fascinated by his chronic condition and the mind-body connection. I truly believe that much of his physical pain at that time was a result of the mental and emotional stress that the IVF was causing. He was adrift, completely outside of his comfort zone, and with that, he had zero grounding. I did what I could to help him by way of Reiki and yoga therapy, but I knew that his back would eventually get better once our future was clearer.

THE DAY OF THE TEST

As D-day finally approached, I was excited about what lay ahead. I could still feel the energy of new life within me and I had this knowingness that all was well. Still, that didn't stop me sleeping fitfully the night before I was due to take the pregnancy test. I woke regularly to check the time and the energy of the embryos in my tummy; I was longing for morning to arrive. It's always the same; the more you long for morning, the longer it takes to arrive.

By 5.30a.m., E and I had both had quite enough and were keen to just get it over with. I felt the energy of the new life in my tummy before leaping out of bed and almost running to the bathroom. I had butterflies and was shaking a little. I re-read the information pack on the testing kit, even though I had read it fully the day before and probably the day before that too, wanting to ensure that I didn't make a mistake and waste it.

There was nothing more for it than to pee on the stick for the allocated time, which I did before replacing the cap and joining E back in the bedroom. I immediately passed him the stick as I didn't want to have to check the result myself. I remember doing the same with my degree result; I didn't want to be the first one to find out, I wanted someone else to take the responsibility!

E timed the two minutes on his watch, as we both sat anxiously, not really knowing what to do with ourselves. I suspect I fussed around a little, tidying or something, I don't really remember. I do know that it felt like an awfully long time.

Finally, the two minutes was up and I hid my head in E's chest as he looked at the test and told me what I already knew – I was pregnant! I could have danced with joy. The IVF had worked and I was jubilant! E was absolutely relieved. I couldn't stop smiling and just wanted to tell the world! *Phew*!

As it happened, I did immediately call my parents to share our good news. We had told our family and friends that we had to wait the whole 14 days until we would know if I was pregnant (it was actually only a 12-day wait). It was important to us that we were able to enjoy this moment together without anyone pressurising us for the result. It was also lovely to be able to surprise them early in the morning – they were going to be grandparents again.

We decided that we would tell those friends and family members who had known we were undertaking IVF, but we wouldn't let anyone else know until we'd had the 12-week scan, and were considered "safely" pregnant. We were also keen that those people who did know before the 12-week scan didn't share our news with others, so as not to jinx the pregnancy!

PART 2

Pregnancy

Chapter 9

Twins?

It was a strange few weeks after I found out I was pregnant.

I was technically four weeks pregnant the day we took the test, with 36 weeks to go until the estimated due date, based on a gestation period of 40 weeks. I found it difficult to get my head around this initially, because I'd always been led to believe that a pregnancy lasts nine months, which it does in terms of when you find out you are pregnant (and have therefore missed a period), but officially, it is counted from the date of your last period, or the date of whichever part of your IVF cycle mimics this.

We were due a scan between six to seven weeks to confirm the pregnancy and to determine whether I was still carrying the two embryos implanted – an embryo is defined as the developing pregnancy from time of fertilisation until the end of the eighth week of gestation, when it becomes known as the foetus. Other than the scan, we had now completed the IVF process and life was strangely quiet.

I know I'm not the only lady to have gone through IVF and found this transition challenging. You go from following a rigid treatment session and receiving an awful amount of attention to all of that suddenly stopping. It felt a little like being in limbo. I was pregnant, but didn't feel any different to how I normally felt – in those early days of pregnancy, post IVF, there was no indication to me or to anyone else that life was significantly changing.

Herm retreat

Life continued much as usual, and the day after finding out I was pregnant, I was leading my bi-annual Yoga & Wellbeing Retreat on the Island of Herm, a 20-minute boat journey from Guernsey. Fortunately, my mum had taken care of much of the organising for me, so it was less stressful than it might have been ordinarily. Retreats are incredibly uplifting, so it felt like it was perfectly timed, even if you're the one facilitating.

There is something about the collective energy of bringing people together with the common purpose of practicing yoga and increasing their sense of wellbeing that always leaves me feeling high spirited. Besides, Herm is a fabulous place to retreat as you cannot help but feel more deeply connected to nature and the elements when you spend time there; it's grounding and healing.

Also, I loved the fact that the embryos were already being bathed in this beautiful Herm yoga retreat energy at four weeks' gestation. Not that I would ever know how this would affect their development or influence their growth or personality in the future, but I liked that yoga and Reiki had been in their lives since conception – it felt complementary to their lightness, to immerse them in the lightness of the energies of these spiritual and healing practices.

The weekend was wonderful and I was on a massive high, just knowing I was pregnant. Perhaps because of this, I experienced one of those moments where everything just felt right. It was Saturday afternoon between classes, and I was practicing yoga on my own in the main studio space in front of views of the sea and the east coast of Guernsey. Deva Premal's beautiful voice filled the room and there was the faint smell of sandalwood in the air.

I sat on my mat with my hands on my tummy so that I could feel the energy of the embryos inside me. All of a sudden, I was overcome with an incredible and momentary feeling of peace. It was a split second; it came and went so quickly. But, in that moment, I felt expansive and aware that absolutely everything was as it was meant to be. All was well. It's the most magnificent feeling of utter joy and peace that happens so infrequently that the moments become memorable.

Poor E, on the other hand, while jubilant that the IVF had worked, was still struggling with his back, to the extent that he was now using a stick to help him walk. The fact that we didn't know if I was carrying one or two embryos was weighing heavily on him. I was convinced I was pregnant with twins, because I had no reason to doubt otherwise, and while I was anxious about how this would play out during pregnancy and birth, I didn't give it too much consideration beyond then. E, however, was constantly questioning how we would cope with two babies in our lives.

Those two weeks between the retreat and the scan seemed to drag on. E started seeing a new doctor who was adamant that he didn't need surgery, so he was feeling a little more positive and empowered; the fear was losing its grip a little. Still, we were both anxious about the scan, and we tried to keep the energy light as we sat in the MSG waiting area for our appointment. By then, I was then six weeks and two days pregnant.

I could still feel the energy inside me, albeit denser now than it had been at the beginning, so I was feeling confident. Mr Nzewi was delighted that I was pregnant and didn't waste any time in getting me scanned. It was yet another transvaginal ultrasound, as this is the safest and clearest way of seeing an embryo at this very early stage of pregnancy. At six weeks' gestation, an embryo is generally between 5-9 mm long, which is very tiny.

So there I was again, legs in stirrups, as the specialist inserted a probe up into my vagina. I was getting a little sick of all these internal scans by now. Still, I didn't have too much time to reflect, because all of a sudden, we were able to see a heart beating on the screen to my side. A heart beating! It was truly incredible. There on the screen, at six weeks' gestation, was the tiniest little heart beating away very quickly, double the rate of an adult heart. I'll never forget this.

E and I looked at each other, huge smiles on our faces. This was real, and there on the screen was the heart to prove it, a heart created by the love and union of our hearts. It was amazing. Certainly, I would never have chosen the path of IVF if we had been able to conceive naturally, yet here we were, because of the IVF, able to witness new life like this. It was a privilege and a joy.

In the spiritual world, we talk of all life being about love, and here to prove this – to me at least – was the image of our six-week-old embryo as a single beating heart. I was beginning to recognise the blessings in the challenge that is conception through IVF. As an energy worker, I was continuously learning about the energetics of new life, of all life, of the purity of the energy of love – the heart beating on the screen proved this to me. We are all heart; there is only love.

However, we'd only seen one visible heart, and while the specialist managed to find what looked like the sack of the other embryo, there was no heart beating. Still, there was hope, as he advised that it might be just a little bit too early to detect a heartbeat, so we'd need to check again after a week or so. Either that or the second embryo hadn't made it.

I knew as he said those words that there wasn't going to be another one. But I wasn't ready to accept it just then. I'd had my heart set on twins. I hadn't considered that we might lose one of the embryos, as everything else had gone to plan. It was a weird feeling. On the one hand, I was ecstatic about seeing the growing embryo, the heart beat within me, and delighted that I was pregnant with this new life, but also strangely upset at the potential loss of the other one.

THE SECOND SCAN

We ended up having to wait a further two weeks for the next scan, and in many respects, this was ideal. It gave me a little time to process things. I still had hope that I was carrying twins, but at the same time, I was also aware that this was unlikely to be a reality. It was another weird limbo time, although by now, I was experiencing morning sickness, so the reality of the pregnancy was hitting home. We were due to go away on holiday the day after the scan, so by the time it came around, I was just keen to know.

It was a different specialist this time, so no stirrups. This was a blessing – it seems they all have their own way of doing things. I doubt there is any lady comfortable with legs in stirrups. It's insane to me to think that women used to have to give birth in this position, but that's another story. For now, it was all about the second embryo, and sadly, it seemed that it had indeed died. I was pregnant with what was now a healthy, growing foetus, and that was that.

I was upset. It sounds ridiculous, I know. I was very lucky; I had a healthy foetus inside me, and I realise that some ladies don't even get that opportunity. But for all intents and purposes, I had miscarried, and that hurt. I questioned whether I had done something wrong. Although I stopped playing netball when I was doing the IVF, I ended up playing in a competitive inter-island game (between Guernsey and Jersey) not long after finding out I was pregnant to help them out, and I wondered whether that might have created the loss. Or perhaps I should have practiced yoga differently. All these thoughts ran through my head.

Until that point, I'd never really understood how women could feel loss over an early pregnancy miscarriage. But now I understood. It doesn't matter how that embryo was conceived, or the period of its gestation; you can still create an immediate emotional bond with it, as you excitedly imagine your future with a new baby in it. To have that then taken away from you, or at least to feel that this is then taken away from you, is heart-breaking.

I have no idea how women cope when they repeatedly miscarry. It must be soul destroying. I felt a new level of respect for all the ladies I knew who had miscarried. It was humbling to gain this new level of awareness. The Universe works in mysterious ways at times. The IVF journey was not something I would have chosen as an opportunity for spiritual growth, but that was exactly what it was presenting to me.

Not only was I encouraged to be more open-minded and do a whole 360 turn on my perception of the medical world and science, so that I had a new level of respect for both, but I was being encouraged to open my mind and be less judgemental. Through my experiences, I was also learning a lot about the energetics of new life, initial pregnancy and loss, so this may make me a more aware and compassionate yoga teacher, healer, and indeed, human being.

My life was taking on a new direction in more ways than one. I was now eight weeks and two days pregnant, and I was certainly feeling the changes in my body. My breasts were heavy and achy, my nose was super sensitive to smell, I experienced an overwhelming sense of tiredness, and I felt nauseous and yucky. *Urgh!* It was incredibly unsettling, but also reassuring to know that the embryo was working its magic and my body was adjusting to the new growth.

I visited my GP to formally advise her that I was pregnant and to enter into another system, the pregnancy one this time. My doctor was delighted for us and sent me away with a pack of information to add to the pile of books I had waiting for me at home. It was clearly time to educate myself on pregnancy and birth. One thing I already knew, however, was that I really wanted a vaginal homebirth, so that the birth could be as natural and non-medicalised as possible. That was my new mission…

CHAPTER 10

Morning Sickness in Thailand, Doulas and Independent Midwives

Long haul travelling during the first trimester, when you are already feeling quite yucky, is certainly no fun. I was eight weeks pregnant and feeling decidedly nauseous and ever so tired at this stage.

I loved the idea of resting for 12 hours in an aeroplane seat, but in reality, even this was exhausting. It was challenging too, simply because of the terrible aeroplane smells and the fact I couldn't elevate my ankles. E was going through his own challenges; his back was still playing up so sitting in an air-seat for that length of time was certainly not easy for him either.

At Bangkok, we had to transfer up to Chiang Mai. We'd both just settled into the seats of the smaller internal plane, when E started panicking that he couldn't find his wallet in his bag. He'd taken it out of his pocket only minutes earlier to put through the scanner at security before we got on the plane. He called the airhostess over, and before I knew it, he was leaving the plane and arranging to join me in Chiang Mai on the next flight.

Without really thinking, I quickly handed him my wallet with all my cards in it, in case anything happened to him, and sent him off on his way, thinking to myself how crazy that here I was, now travelling up to Chiang Mai on my own, pregnant, and with no wallet. One does silly things in the heat of the moment!

At Chiang Mai Airport, the driver, who would be taking E and I to the house where my folks and my brother and his family would later join us, met me. I'm not sure he was that delighted to hear that we now had to sit around the airport, waiting for E's plane, which was due to land within the next two hours, but alas, there wasn't much we could do about it.

By then, I was feeling surprisingly OK. It was like the jet lag has somehow managed to shift the sickness I had previously been feeling. It was incredibly humid in the airport and I sat, trying to read my book, feeling thankful that at least I had a bottle of water to drink because I had no money to actually buy anything – this is a really horrible feeling and made me feel very vulnerable.

After 20 minutes or so, I had cause to rummage in my bag, and lo and behold, there was E's wallet. Argh! My phone wasn't working at that point so I wasn't able to call him and let him know, and I hoped that he'd still gotten on the next plane and wasn't trawling Bangkok airport for his supposed lost wallet!

Fortunately, he arrived on the next flight from Bangkok and we both laughed at the ridiculousness of the situation. It turned out that the kind staff at Bangkok airport had replayed the security camera footage, showing E putting his wallet through the security belt, so they'd been able to see that he'd popped it into my bag at the end of the belt. Crazy man with his short-term memory, and me completely unaware of the fact he had put his wallet into my bag, which doesn't bode well, does it, at least for personal security?

PEACE IN THAILAND

In any event, all was resolved and sorted, and we were then driven the hour or so up into the hills to the house we had rented for the next two weeks. The house was situated in a marvellous spot in the middle of nowhere really, and had its own staff, which was pure luxury for me, as it meant someone else was cooking. However, what I hadn't factored in was the fact that we would be eating Thai food at every meal, and that no one had thought to tell the staff that I was essentially a vegetarian, so the meat dishes served upon arrival were a touch challenging!

Those first 24 hours were relatively easy going for me. There was a welcoming outdoor swimming pool where we could all cool off from the intense humidity, and the rooms had air conditioning (which only worked sometimes). This didn't matter so much as the house itself was relatively cool. I was beginning to think that perhaps the morning sickness had eased, but after that initial 24-hour period, I was left with no doubt that the morning sickness was still very much there.

Morning sickness sucks! Yes, I know, I should have been very grateful for the fact that I was even experiencing morning sickness because that meant I'm pregnant and I was grateful, truly I was. And I'm quite sure that when I was having trouble conceiving, I got sick of hearing other pregnant ladies moan about their sickness and about their indigestion and tiredness and all the other stuff that pregnancy entails.

But the truth is, morning sickness is the most debilitating thing I have ever experienced. And to be honest, unless you've gone through it, I don't think you can ever truly understand how absolutely awful it is. For a start, the term "*morning sickness*" is utterly ridiculous. Whoever thought this one up was clearly someone who has never experienced it, because yes, while I did indeed feel sick in the morning, I was also feeling sick throughout the rest of the day too.

I'm not usually one for eating breakfast, but in Thailand, I just absolutely had to have something inside my tummy, and fruit just wouldn't do the job. Ordinarily, I give bread a wide berth, as it doesn't agree with me, but this was probably the only thing that made me feel even slightly better – tea and a piece of toast with jam and butter, two other ingredients that never usually pass my lips – and I admit to feeling guilty about this.

It's crazy really, this whole guilt thing, and I know that I'm not alone in feeling it. I'm a keen fan of good nutrition and I've done a lot of work on myself with this in terms of discovering what works best for me in how it makes me feel – we are what we eat, after all. So, the fact my cravings were challenging that was actually challenging me too. While it may seem like no big deal to many, the fact I was eating bread was a big deal to me, and I couldn't shake the feeling that I was being unhealthy somehow.

It got worse though, because about an hour after breakfast, lying by the pool, I would start feeling incredibly sick, and absolutely the only thing that seemed to ease this feeling was drinking a very cold can of sparkling lemon pop, which no doubt contained vast quantities of sugar, let alone all the other horrible stuff that gets added to soft drinks. I just couldn't believe that a drink like this could possibly make me feel better, but amazingly, it did – and this was before 10 o'clock in the morning. Yikes, what was going on with my body?

Now ordinarily, up until that point, I had always loved Thai food. But laying out by the pool, those first few mornings, the smell of the Thai food being prepared for lunch was enough to turn my stomach and make me feel wretched. Let alone then sitting at the table and being offered a full, cooked Thai meal. In fairness, even E and my folks were challenged by two Thai meals a day, and it was with some relief that we agreed to prepare our own lunch and just eat one main Thai meal in the evening.

All I really wanted to eat was bread with goat's cheese and tomatoes. Fortunately, the Western supermarket that we found in Chiang Mai provided all of these ingredients, so we stocked up and that pretty much kept me going at lunchtime. In the afternoon, I'd get a full on fruit craving, the sweeter the better. I recall E and I being in Chiang Mai one afternoon, when it was particularly hot, and all I wanted was a smoothie, with as much ice as possible, the colder the better, but they never seemed to be cold enough and never truly quenched my thirst.

Late afternoon, I would experience a lull in sickness, which was a welcome relief, and I would look forward to aperitif time, not for the wine – I certainly couldn't stomach that – but for the salted nuts and crisps that were on offer. Now, all I wanted to eat was salt, washed down with ice-cold sparkling water. Salted nuts and crisps were usually a big no-no on my list, but now I couldn't get enough of them!

And then, dinnertime would come and my stomach would turn once again. I don't know what it was but the smell of Thai food just made me feel sick. It didn't help that my brother's fiancé developed a love of textured soya protein, so we ended up having various kinds of it as the base (if not the only constituent part) of our vegetarian meals throughout our stay, and I just absolutely could not stand it. Even now, the thought of it makes me feel sick. Thankfully, I was able to eat rice, and that was really the main staple for me at those meals.

Still, nausea and food aside, it was a great trip. I was incredibly tired during much of it, but of course, I could indulge in lying by the pool and chilling out without having anyone else to think about but myself. I even managed to enjoy a couple of massages and attend a few yoga classes in Chiang Mai, which always eased my sickness. I also joined E and the folks on a walk through a National Park, although sadly, I had to give the zip wire/tree walking a miss, as it wasn't suitable for pregnant ladies.

DOING MY HOMEWORK

It was whilst I was in Thailand that I started reading up on birth. A few years earlier, I had trained as a pregnancy yoga teacher with a lovely lady, who lived in Surrey, and who was very passionate about home and vaginal birth. She had certainly inspired me with her tales and had directed me to a few books, which she highly recommended, on the subject. One of these was called *Birthing from Within* by Pam England and Rob Horowitz, which I had read previously, in terms of educating myself to be able to assist my students, and I had lent the book to a number of them, who found it very inspiring. Now, here I was, reading it for myself, and I too was inspired.

I had been given another book called *Gentle Birth, Gentle Mothering* by Sarah Buckley, which was also interesting, especially in terms of the various scans and tests that are carried out during pregnancy, and she also advocated a natural approach to birth. My brother's fiancé is also a pregnancy yoga teacher and helps to facilitate pregnancy yoga teacher training courses. She is also very passionate about home birthing, having birthed my niece at home with an independent midwife and doula present, so she was keen to educate me on this too.

I was aware that I was now entering a whole new world and that there was a lot yet to learn. While I had the time, I emailed our local doula, Anita, back in Guernsey to share news of my pregnancy and to enquire into her availability for the birth, and to find out more about access to independent midwives in Guernsey. Little did I know how much she would inspire me and how passionate I would become about birth.

The word *doula* comes from the ancient Greek, meaning "*a woman who serves*", and is now used to refer to a woman experienced in childbirth, who guides women and their partners through the process of preparing for birth, supporting them during labour and the birth, and subsequent bonding with the newborn. A birth doula recognises birth as a key experience that the mother will remember all her life.

She understands the physiology of birth and the emotional needs of a woman in labour, and assists the woman in preparing for and carrying out her plans for birth. She stays with the woman throughout her labour (if this is her choice), providing emotional support, physical comfort and an objective viewpoint, as well as helping the woman obtain the information she needs to make informed decisions.

She also facilitates communication between the labouring woman, her partner and her clinical care providers. She perceives her role as nurturing and protecting the woman's memory of the birth experience and allows the woman's partner to participate at his/her comfort level. Studies have shown that when doulas attend births, labours are shorter and have fewer complications, babies are healthier and they breastfeed more easily.

A doula can also offer her services postpartum, so that she provides companionship and non-judgmental support during the fourth trimester. Here, she can provide evidence-based information on emotional and physical recovery from birth, infant feeding, infant soothing and coping skills for new parents, as well as making appropriate referrals when necessary. In short, she is an angel, and I was keen to have as many angels as I could in my life.

An independent midwife is also an angel, but in a different way. She is someone who has chosen to work outside the hospital service in a self-employed and private capacity to provide pregnancy care. The legal role of a midwife encompasses the care of women and babies during pregnancy, birth (and homebirth), as well as the early weeks of motherhood. Usually, just one private midwife gives care to a woman and her family throughout a pregnancy and you can expect to pay for the service accordingly.

Thus, having established a trusting relationship, the same independent midwife cares for the woman as she births her baby and supports the family afterwards. Research has shown that many women want this type of midwifery and pregnancy care, which they do not always receive from their local health care provider, and that it helps women to cope with the challenges of labour and the transition to parenthood.

The vast majority of births attended by independent midwives are homebirths, but they can also be present at planned hospital births too. Independent midwives have more freedom to practice individualised care, compared to those working within the hospital environment, who may be restricted by guidelines and protocols.

Independent midwives are still regulated by the Nursing and Midwifery Council, and they are subject to the same supervision as those midwives working in hospitals. They are required to keep up to date with their practice, and are only allowed to act within their sphere of competence as midwives.

For me, as the conception had been so medicalised, I was keen to ensure that the birth was as natural as possible. I wanted to avoid any intervention, especially as I was aware that intervention can lead to more intervention and to a potentially medicalised birthing experience. I was very aware how, over time, birth has become a medicalised experience, and as a result of this, the emphasis has shifted from the mother to the baby, so that the mother was – and in many cases, continues to be – overlooked in the whole birthing experience.

As Dr Christiane Northrup writes in her marvellous book (which every lady should read) *Women's Bodies, Women's Wisdom*:

"*Labour and delivery often go well. Yet as a society, we continue to treat the normal process of birth with hysteria. High anxiety about pregnancy and birth is partly the result of our collective unresolved birth trauma – nearly every one of us has unfinished business about her or his own birth that we keep projecting on to pregnant women. Most baby boomers, after all, were born drugged and were whisked away from their mothers to the glaring lights and sterility of the hospital nursery. The Second World War generation was born at home. Then birth became medicalised and moved into the hospital. Though the mortality rate fell, we lost a great deal of birthing wisdom with this shift. I have seen cemeteries strewn with the headstones of women who died young, surrounded by the graves of their dead children. Most of these deaths and traumas resulted from poor nutrition, overwork and lack of maternal support, not necessarily from lack of sophisticated medical intervention.*"

The trouble is, these days, birth often involves some form of intervention, which in many cases is probably unnecessary but sadly part of what's accepted as normal. For example, studies show that most of the women in the UK will have experienced at least one of the following routine medical interventions:

- Caesarean section
- Induction
- Artificial rupture of membranes
- Continuous electronic foetal monitoring
- Epidural anaesthesia, episiotomy and recumbent birthing position

The more I read, the more I began to discover that childbirth has become an increasingly medicalised phenomenon, whereby the majority of women no longer experience or have knowledge of what it is to give birth to their baby without interference. It would seem that almost all women who give birth in hospital are subjected to a cascade of medical and technological interventions throughout pregnancy and birth.

I researched a little further and discovered that since 1985, the international healthcare community has considered the ideal rate for caesarean sections to be between 10-15% (see World Health Organization). However, statistics collated by the NHS for 2013-14 showed that the caesarean rate was nearer to 26.2%.

I also discovered that, when medically necessary, a caesarean section can effectively prevent maternal and new-born mortality. Two new studies show that when caesarean section rates rise towards 10% across a population, the number of maternal and new-born deaths decreases. However, when the rate goes above 10%, there is no evidence that mortality rates decrease any further. Thus, while a caesarean section clearly has its place in preventing death to mother and/or baby during birth, there comes a point whereby having a caesarean section isn't just about the safety of mother and baby during birth (as it may have initially been intended).

As Dr Christiane Northrup further writes, "*The medical system participates fully in treating childbirth as an emergency needing a cure. Because of its addictive, patriarchal nature, the medical system becomes the symbolic 'husband' for all women crying, 'Jerry, do something!' And believe me, doctors are trained in many ways to 'do something'. Each of our doings has a price. Some studies show, for instance, that epidural anaesthesia increase the rate of caesarean section because this anaesthesia relaxes the pelvic floor muscles, causing the baby to engage with the head in what's called the occiput posterior position – facing up. It's much harder to push a baby out when she is in this position; it also slows down the process and may add to the baby's distress. Epidurals are also a metaphor for current mind/body split approach to childbirth: 'I want to be awake and intellectually aware, but I don't want to feel my body.'"*

I researched further and found that NHS statistics for the period 2013-14 also show a continuing upward trend in induction rates, increasing by 1.7% during that year to 25%. The World Health Organization recommends induction of labour should only be performed when there's a clear medical indication for it, and the expected benefits outweigh its potential harms.

In applying the recommendations, the World Health Organization says that consideration must be given to the actual condition, wishes and preferences of each woman, with emphasis being placed on cervical status, the specific method of induction of labour, and associated conditions such as parity and rupture of membranes. They recommend that induction of labour should only be performed with caution, since the procedure carries the risk of uterine hyper-stimulation and rupture and foetal distress.

And yet, it seems that induction has become commonplace. I've lost count of the number of times I have heard of women being induced and being deprived of the opportunity to connect with their body wisdom and allow their body to do what it needs to do naturally. They are continuously monitored, and in effect, strapped to a bed so that they cannot move or allow their bodies the opportunity to find the optimal position for birth.

Before they know it, they have agreed to an epidural and then can't feel what their body is doing; they are full of fear and the baby senses this, and the medical staff are concerned about the signs of foetal distress. Hands then begin probing to check for thinning/contracting of cervix, and electrodes are placed on the baby's head.

Is it any surprise that the baby gets distressed? It's been happy in there for 40 weeks (or whatever the term is) of its growing life, safely protected by Mum, and now here it is, being probed before it has even entered the world. Plus, of course, it can sense poor Mum's fear and the stress that accompanies this.

Thus, it follows that the mother is no longer capable of birthing her baby and she is wheeled down to theatre to have her baby extracted, born into the bright lights and sterility of such an environment, in front of strangers who know nothing of her and nor her of them. Welcome to the world baby, what a way to begin!

By this stage, as the mother, you're just delighted and relieved that your baby's arrived safely and everyone keeps telling you this. You try to put aside any concerns that there's something wrong with your body that means that it cannot birth vaginally, and try not to reflect on how different things could be. The baby's safe, that's all that matters...

But here's the thing, of course, it goes without saying that you want to birth a healthy baby, but at some point, the care shifted from it being also about the mum to just being about the baby, and that's unfortunate really. The medical model of childbirth assumes that the female body is always ready to fail.

So it follows, that childbirth is now seen as a highly risky business. The majority of women who give birth in hospital do so because they assume that a hospital birth is safest. However, all the research evidence that exists demonstrates that, for a healthy woman with a normal pregnancy, a planned homebirth is as safe as a hospital birth (BirthChoiceUK, 2005). In spite of this research, not everybody agrees, and many healthcare professionals insist on claiming that a medicalised hospital birth is still the safest option.

Reactions to the medicalisation of birth have been various. For some women, the technology and surveillance that is brought to bear on the birthing body is welcomed as a comforting presence to help ensure that the baby remains safe and well.

Whilst it is essential that this is recognised, one has to question the underlying reason for the practice, in terms of litigation and making life easier for medical staff. For example, a reason women are encouraged to birth on their backs, even though this makes no sense physiologically and will only serve to make the whole process much more challenging and much more painful, is because it makes it easier for medical staff to see what is going on.

As Dr Christiane Northrup writes, "*During my training, when foetal monitoring came in and the Caesarean section rate began to soar, I remember thinking, 'How can it be that 25% of women aren't able to go through a normal physiological event without the aid of anaesthesia and major surgery? How could the human race have possibly survived if this many women really need major surgery to give birth? What is going wrong here?' I was taught that I must treat everyone as though she was going to have a potential complication, as if normal labour could turn into crisis at a moment's notice. Whenever a woman arrived in labour, we immediately put in an intravenous drip, took blood, ruptured her membranes – broke the amniotic sac ('bag of waters') surrounding the baby – screwed a foetal scalp electrode into the baby's head and threaded a catheter into the mother's uterus to measure intra-uterine pressure on the foetal monitor. Then she and her family, the doctors and the nurses, all fixed their gazes on the monitor and pretty much relied on it to tell us what to do next. The women were asked to labour in a position that gave the best monitor tracing – not the one that felt best to her...*

... Later, studies would show that foetal monitoring did not actually improve perinatal outcome when compared with a nurse listening to the heart rate periodically. What it did do was increase Caesarean section rates – a great example of technology 'catching on' before all the data were in. (Monitoring has its place – I'm not against it. It simply is not a substitute for caring, human interaction, though it is often used as one)...

Unfortunately, the beliefs that support hospital procedures are often so pervasive that even those women who enter hospital wanting natural childbirth often end up with some kind of intervention. This is because a woman in labour is highly vulnerable. If she is not supported in her labour process by people who truly trust labour and see it as normal, she can be talked in to just about anything."

Taking this all into consideration, it wasn't perhaps surprising that I was keen to do all I could to promote a straightforward homebirth with people around me who supported me and believed in the wisdom and power of my body. I imagined birthing at home in the peace and quiet of my own spiritual space, providing me with the opportunity to truly tap into my body's innate wisdom and trust in that.

I felt that to have the chance of achieving this, I would benefit from employing the services of an independent and intuitive midwife, with whom I could establish a close and indeed trusting relationship, and a doula, who would be able to attend to my needs before, during and after birth. Anita was my chosen doula, and she was delighted to take on that role.

Unfortunately, there isn't an independent midwife in Guernsey, so I knew that I would need to engage the services of an independent midwife from England. Anita kindly put me in contact with an independent midwife friend, who certainly sounded ideal, but I quickly realised that it was going to cost us a lot of money, not least in terms of her fee for the delivery itself, approximately £3,000 (quite understandable incidentally), but in terms of the fact we would need to establish a relationship, which would mean paying for flights backwards and forwards between the UK and Guernsey (a flight costs approximately £150–£200 a return trip).

Furthermore, the independent midwife would need to be on the island well in advance of the due date and we would need to provide her with accommodation during this period at our expense (on Guernsey, accommodation is expensive!). I discussed the matter with E but he was not keen. I must admit, the thought of having someone in our space for the weeks leading up to the birth didn't resonate with me, as I am very precious about my need for space, and especially at home.

All in all, we didn't feel that we could justify the expense of the independent midwife and I would have to take my chances with whoever happened to be on shift at the time. My mind, however, was absolutely set on Anita as my doula, and while E was a little resistant due to the fact he wasn't sure of the role he would play in the birth, I was keen to make sure I was booked up and could be assured of her presence on D-day!! So that was that decided while we were away!

Chapter 11

Miscarrying?

Almost 11 weeks pregnant, and our departure from Thailand was memorable, simply because the morning sickness was at what I hoped would be its peak. We spent our last night staying at a rather lovely hotel in the centre of Chiang Mai, and in the morning, we joined the main dining room for breakfast. E loves breakfast and was incredibly excited about the extensive choice, from Eastern food, to the continental buffet style that we are used to back home, but it was all I could do not to throw up upon arrival.

The smell of the Eastern food was just too much for me and I sat at our table, desperately trying to chew small bites of plain toast without vomiting. I knew that without food in my stomach, I was likely to feel worse during the rest of the morning, but it was an effort. It sounds crazy to anyone who has never gone through it themselves; this concept of eating something to ease the feeling of sickness, but for me, it made a huge difference.

The flight back to the UK was equally challenging, as the smell of the aeroplane food exacerbated the feeling of nausea. Strangely, fruity Mentos sweets seemed to help. E was surprised as he'd never seen me eat a sweet, and here I was, obsessed with them! It did seem like the strangest craving, all that sugar and artificial flavourings, but it made a huge difference.

Back in the UK, we spent a night staying at a hotel near Heathrow Airport. Jet lag and morning sickness do not combine well, and that next morning, I felt rotten. It didn't help that we had to travel into central London to catch a train across the country, to Manchester Airport. Here, we had pre-booked a hire car, so that we could drive to a wedding that Saturday in St Martin's, a few hours' drive south.

LISTENING TO MY BODY

It was Friday lunchtime by the time we got to the central London train station. The sun was shining brightly and there was a jovial end-of-the-working-week atmosphere in the air as people milled about, eating their lunch. I left E sitting in the sun while I spent a good 30 minutes walking from one sandwich shop to another, and back again, studying the sandwiches in some depth, to determine which one may make me feel better.

I wasn't used to buying sandwiches, as I don't usually eat bread, and here I was, salivating at the mere sight of them. As a non-dairy eating vegetarian, I was particularly humoured by the fact I was repeatedly attracted to both roast beef sandwiches and cheese and pickle sandwiches. It was the strangest thing, because my head was saying "absolutely no!" and yet my body was crying out, "yes, yes, yes!"

It made me realise how much I was still listening to my head when it came to choosing food, and not to my body, and therefore, how much my old eating disorder was still having an influence on my present-day food choices. It seemed that pregnancy was well and truly throwing me out of my comfort zone, as it was making me question my usual habitual way of eating, and that was, at times, challenging.

Needless to say, E was wondering where I was and couldn't believe it had taken me so long to buy a couple of sandwiches. The cheese and pickle sandwich won out in the end, together with a packet of crisps and a sugary sparkling lemon drink. I kept thinking to myself, this is ridiculous, here I am growing new life inside me, I should really be eating a super healthy diet, but actually, all I want to eat is unhealthy stuff instead.

Cheese sandwich or not, I felt desperately sick much of the train journey. I had bought myself one of those awful celebrity magazines at the train station that provide meaningless distraction when travelling. This particular magazine contained an article about miscarriage, which I found slightly unnerving and which, for some strange reason, kept drawing my attention. Little did I realise how poignant this would become the next morning.

It was a relief to make it to the hotel later that early evening and crawl into bed to sleep. Ordinarily, I love travelling, but I was finding it hard work while pregnant. It was hardly surprising; your body is going through such a lot of change that first trimester. Not only did I feel sick, but also my breasts were growing and my waist had thickened, so I was beginning to feel uncomfortable in my usual clothing. I was also looking pale and washed out, despite my Thai suntan.

Bleeding

The next morning, I awoke feeling decidedly out of sorts. I joined E for breakfast in the small hotel dining room and attempted to eat some toast, while he tucked into a hot breakfast. It was then that I started experiencing lower stomach cramps that had me holding my lower tummy. I was hoping it was just trapped wind, but something didn't feel right, and I started channelling Reiki onto my lower tummy in the hope that the combination of this and the toast and tea may ease things.

But alas not, and back in our room, I went to the toilet, only to find that I was discharging brown blood. Panic quickly took hold. I immediately imagined the worst and was overcome with that horrible stomach-churning, empty feeling, as I started shaking uncontrollably. Everything became very real and very present-moment, like time stood still. I couldn't believe I was discharging brown blood and I cried out to E in the bedroom before bursting into tears.

I didn't know what to do. I was desperately trying to feel the energy of the foetus inside me but I was too panicky to know what I was feeling. I reached for my laptop and googled "*brown blood 11 weeks pregnant*". This probably wasn't the best idea, as I came across a whole host of pregnancy forums, where women shared their experiences of miscarriage. Fear kicked in. That's the trouble with these websites; they're very fear-driven.

I couldn't quite believe I might be miscarrying. It seemed too cruel. Having beaten the odds to get pregnant through IVF, to then miscarry, was desperately unfair. It hadn't even crossed my mind that this may happen. I was taking the progesterone pessaries to support the pregnancy and just figured that would help to prevent miscarriage.

I used my pendulum to try to dowse for the energy of the foetus. Ordinarily, using a pendulum helps me to check in with my intuition, but I was feeling so anxious and desperate that I couldn't determine my truth. There was a part of me that was hopeful that because the blood was brown, and not bright red, that all would be well. But I was cramping and the discharge was noticeable, so I couldn't ignore that something was happening, even if I didn't yet know exactly what it was.

We were due to collect E's best friend from the train station later that morning and I decided that I would go with him, as I didn't want to be left on my own. I lay still on the bed, channelling Reiki onto my tummy until we had to leave. The discharge had eased a little by then but I was still getting cramps and I just felt that I needed to get it checked out. So after collecting E's friend, we headed to the local A&E department.

It was only a small department and they weren't able to offer me a scan to check for the foetal heartbeat until the Monday, by which time we would be back home in Guernsey. The doctor was very kind but did little to ease my concerns. My symptoms suggested a miscarriage, but he said that there was little they could do for me, and advised me to go home and rest.

There was something that didn't feel right about this. Waiting in the hospital environment had given me the opportunity to calm myself with my breath and drop out of panic mode. I kept trying to feel the energy of the foetus inside me, and now that my mind was calmer, I began to sense something again. I had a feeling I was still pregnant, but couldn't be sure whether I may later miscarry. It was a whole new world to me.

E and I discussed whether I should stay at the hotel, but I decided to join the wedding, as I needed a distraction. It was a tough day, though, and while the wedding was lovely, a small, intimate affair, I found it difficult to concentrate and engage in any meaningful conversation. My mind was distracted by the sensations I was feeling in my body, and I couldn't stop trying to feel the energy of the foetus and channel Reiki into it.

The worst bit was the vaginal discharge. As soon as I felt some change in sensation down below, I was immediately desperate to know if it meant I was bleeding. I spent a lot of the day visiting the toilet, but it was with utter dread that I did so, praying as I pulled down my pants that I wouldn't see blood. I can still remember that sickening feeling that accompanied any toilet visit; little did I know that this would set the scene for the rest of the pregnancy.

By the afternoon, I was heartened to find that I was feeling decidedly sick again. Never have I been so delighted to experience morning sickness! Once again, I was going through a U-turn on my perception of things. Conception, and now pregnancy, was throwing everything on its head. If I were still pregnant then I would welcome all sickness from now on. It was a sign of an ongoing pregnancy and that is something I wanted to celebrate.

Chapter 12

Will the Morning Sickness Ever End?

Back home in Guernsey, a day later, the specialist confirmed that I hadn't miscarried. He wasn't entirely sure what it was, but surmised that it may have been the passing of the embryo sack from the embryo that hadn't made it. It was a huge wake-up call to take things a little easier and slow my life down, to appreciate the new life growing inside of me. But this is easier said than done, and the Universe nudged me time and time again…

My tiredness was now all-consuming. I've never known tiredness quite like it; it was all I could do to get through the day.

Prior to the pregnancy, I was a night owl, and thought nothing of staying up until midnight and beyond. But now, I was finding that I absolutely had to be in bed by 9.30p.m., it was unheard of and quite a shift for me. I didn't know how I was going to get everything done, but I had little choice; my body was telling me in no uncertain terms that it absolutely had to rest!

Feeling rough

The morning sickness showed no immediate sign of easing either. I had researched the condition on the Internet and had initially been heartened to read that, for many, morning sickness can peak at about week nine. But here we were, approaching week 12, and I still felt terrible.

It was incredibly challenging, especially with my heightened sensitivity to smell. I struggled with the smell of our cottage, despite cleaning everywhere, even behind and under all the furniture, but still, the smell persisted! I also developed an aversion to my usual loved aromatherapy oil scented candle. Even the slightest whiff of it was enough to make me feel sick.

As for the fridge, well, I developed an absolute aversion to this too, so that it was challenging having to get something from it – crazy isn't it? Imagine feeling sick every time you go to your fridge. Needless to say, cooking was also a trial of sorts, to the extent that I stopped doing it, and E lived, for a while, on anything that was easy to just put in the oven.

Fortunately, my mum made him lots of meals, so it wasn't like he suffered nutritionally – in fact, he probably benefitted, as she is a much better cook than me. The worst thing was being in the office, because at that point, no one knew I was pregnant, and the smell of my colleagues' lunches was often stomach-churning. It didn't help that my desk was near to the kitchen.

As for my lunch, all I wanted to eat was cheese and tomato baguettes and Dorito crisps. I know I keep saying it, but it truly was the strangest thing because I would absolutely never usually eat anything like this and had to ignore the fact I was consuming all these additives, and just surrender to my body's rather strange cravings, let alone all that unhealthy fat.

I appreciated that women often put on weight when pregnant; you're growing a baby after all. But I didn't want to use that as an excuse to "stuff my face", as others had told me they did. Not only did I feel this was unnecessary, but I wanted to stay fit and healthy in preparation for the birth and for life with a baby.

The most disconcerting thing was not knowing how long this was all going to go on. The online pregnancy forums were full of terrible tales of sickness the whole pregnancy, and I knew this had been the case for friends locally. I couldn't even consider this. I've no idea how those women coped and I have every respect. The thought of this sent me into a minor panic and I took comfort in the fact my mum had not suffered sickness throughout the whole of her pregnancies.

The only saving grace was the fact I wasn't actually vomiting, and there was some respite from the sickness in the late afternoon and evening. However, I found that yoga teaching was probably the only time I felt truly OK, simply because I'd be focused on the students and therefore, completely unaware of my own discomfort. Plus, I had no choice but to just get on with it.

Still, the Thursday morning classes, those next few weeks, were tough. I felt really sick and absolutely had to eat something before teaching, and yet this was a challenge, simply because I had conditioned myself never to eat before yoga; it's not something you're encouraged to do as it can lead to digestive issues. Pregnancy was truly testing me in terms of the rules and limitations I had created in my mind around food and yoga.

One of my students said she knew that I was pregnant simply because of the way I looked, all pasty, pale and yucky – I guess you come to recognise this when you've been through it yourself a few times. I know I didn't look my best, and my body was certainly changing shape, and that in itself was challenging because I didn't want people knowing that my bigger breasts and increasing waistline were signs of pregnancy.

Still, the 12-week threshold, when we could finally announce the pregnancy, was soon approaching, and with that, an appointment with the midwife and the 12-week scan. I was aware that the natural approach to pregnancy foregoes the scans, but with the recent miscarriage scare, I felt I needed the comfort of seeing the growing foetus on the screen. It was all very exciting, and as grateful as I was, I really hoped the sickness would ease soon…

Chapter 13

The 12-Week Scan

For many, the 12-week scan is the first time that they get to see their growing baby on a screen. We'd already had a number of scans by this stage, albeit internal vaginal ones, so we were very aware of how exciting it is to see your baby in utero. I shall never forget the mind-blowing nature of our first scan at six weeks' gestation, which showed a simple beating heart, reminding me that we are all about the heart, essentially. Then two weeks later, to re-determine the number of babies I was carrying, and seeing little arm and leg buds, equally amazing.

Sonographers

The 12-week scans tend to be carried out by specially trained staff called sonographers and are conducted in a dimly-lit room so the sonographer can get good images of the baby. At the scan itself, you are asked to lie on a couch and to lower your skirt or trousers to your hips and lift your top to your chest so your abdomen is uncovered. The sonographer, or their assistant, should tuck tissue paper around your clothing to protect it from the gel, which will be put on your tummy.

The sonographer then passes a handheld probe over your skin to enable them to examine the baby's body. The gel makes sure that there is good contact between the probe and your skin, and in theory, a black and white image of the baby will appear on the ultrasound screen. Having the scan doesn't hurt, as such, but the sonographer may need to apply slight pressure to get the best views of the baby, and this can be a little uncomfortable with a full bladder (which is a requirement for the scan – you're given guidelines on how much water to drink, and when).

The sonographer needs to keep the screen in a position that gives them a good view of the baby, so the screen may be directly facing them, or at an angle, but you may have another screen ahead of you so you can see what he or she is doing. Sometimes, the sonographer will need to be quiet while they concentrate on checking the baby; it's good to know this so you don't think they might be being quiet because they have found something worrying. They'll be able to talk to you about the pictures once they have completed the check, and if you're lucky, you also get to take some images home with you – here on Guernsey, you pay for the privilege.

This first scan at 12 weeks is sometimes called the dating scan because the sonographer estimates when the baby is due (the estimated date of delivery), based on the baby's measurements. I already had an idea of my due date because we had an exact date of "conception" from the clinic, so I wasn't sure how a machine could better that really, and it can't, it just provides an estimation. However, a lot can hinge on this estimated date in terms of gestation period (in the case of premature babies, this has quite some implication) and a date that may determine whether you are "overdue" and require induction (and therefore intervention).

I've never been entirely comfortable with the idea of the estimated date. I appreciate that you need to have one, and I appreciate that many women do not know when they actually conceived and therefore need an indication of where they are in their pregnancy, but I'm just not convinced we should get too hung up on the date in terms of delivery.

From my experience, babies arrive when they are ready to arrive and, psychologically, I've seen many women get themselves all worked up when the baby does not arrive on the "due date". They then have induction and intervention hanging over their heads, which can create unnecessary stress.

Furthermore, other people, be that family, friends and/or work colleagues, can become very fixated on a date and add additional pressure to the anticipation of the eagerly awaited birth. Lots of judgments can also arise in terms of the size of bump in relation to the stage of pregnancy, which of course brings with it anxieties, as people – often innocently – comment on how big the baby may be, or how big you are getting carrying the baby – none of this is helpful, especially if you are already anxious about the potential vaginal birth!

Still, here we were, at the dating scan, so it was of course to be expected that we would be given a date, and yes, it turned out to be a few days short of the date we had expected, based on the information provided to us by Wessex. The dating machine determined that our little bean would be expected for delivery on 21st November 2013, nine days short of E's 47th birthday. I decided, however, not to place too much emphasis on this date. The baby would arrive when he or she wanted to arrive, and often, first babies can be notoriously late.

The 12-week scan can also include a Nuchal Translucency (NT) scan, which is part of the combined screening test for Down's syndrome, and involves a blood test and an ultrasound scan. We decided to take the screening test, which basically looks at the risk in the pregnancy of the baby being born with Down's syndrome. It doesn't give a definite "yes" or "no" answer – if the screening test shows a higher risk that the baby has Down's syndrome then you are offered a diagnostic test, to see if the baby actually does have Down's syndrome or not.

The screening involves a scan, where the sonographer measures the fluid collection under the skin at the back of the baby's neck (the nuchal translucency). Apparently, all babies have a collection of fluid here, but babies with Down's syndrome tend to have more fluid in this area. The fluid measurement, your age, the size of the baby, and other details such as your weight, ethnicity and smoking status are then put into a computer programme to give the risk of the baby having Down's syndrome. Sometimes, it can be difficult to obtain an accurate measurement of the nuchal translucency, due to the position of the baby or where the pregnant lady is overweight.

Blood tests may be done to measure levels of various hormones and proteins in your blood (produced by the placenta of the developing baby). If the baby has Down's syndrome, the levels of these substances can be affected. Again, a computer programme is used to give the risk of the baby having Down's syndrome, based on the blood test results, your age, the stage in your pregnancy, your weight, ethnicity and smoking status. This blood test is sometimes called serum screening.

During our scan, our Australian sonographer managed to measure the nuchal translucency, and the result indicated we were low risk. However, we also needed to do the blood test so, following the scan, we walked up to the maternity unit to have bloods taken. The choice to undertake this test is very personal to each parent and should be discussed prior to the scan so that you know where you both stand.

I've known parents elect not to carry out the screening test and they have been perfectly content with their decision. I've also known other parents who have chosen not to take the scan but have then spent the latter part of the pregnancy fretting about whether their child may have Down's syndrome and considering their ability to cope if that happened to be the case. And of course, there are other parents, like us, who felt that we wanted to know, so at least we could try to prepare ourselves mentally, if nothing else.

The scan was excellent. I know there are some who believe that the scans adversely affect the baby, but for us, having already had a number of essential scans with the IVF, we were happy to go with the flow of things. It was actually really exciting, and indeed, emotional, to see a real life baby with a head and arms and legs and organs on the screen. I know that may sound silly because, of course, we already knew that I was carrying a baby inside me, but it became all the more real – we really were having a baby!

However, there was an edge to our scan, simply because the sonographer noted that my placenta was lying low. She told me it was highly likely that it would move upwards as the pregnancy progressed, but there was something about the way she said it, or perhaps the way I heard it, that made me think that I couldn't be so sure.

I didn't know an awful lot about placentas at that point, but I made a mental note to find out all I could when I returned home. Other than that, the scan seemed fine and we left with the classic scan prints, which don't really mean an awful lot to anyone else, but provide you with a memento all the same.

By the time we attended this scan, I was on the waiting list to join my doula, Anita's, pregnancy yoga classes, as they were known at the time. I contacted her following my scan, and she – like the sonographer – reassured me that it was highly likely that the placenta would move as the uterus expanded, and not to worry too much about a low-lying placenta. I decided that I would try to forget about it. I am very aware that we attract that to which we give attention, so better not to give it too much attention!

Settling into pregnancy

I had already met with a midwife for an initial consultation, in which I relayed my intention to have a homebirth. At that time, home birthing was only just becoming a more acceptable option, so there was some mention of the need to check that the cottage was appropriate, and some muttering that if the ward were short-staffed then they would expect me to come into the hospital to birth, and that access to the birthing pool would be dependent on how busy they were in the delivery rooms.

I was still busily reading any book I could get my hands on about homebirth, natural approaches to birth, and birthing without fear. I found it all fascinating, and with my interest in natural approaches to healing and life generally, let alone the whole law of attraction perspective on things, I was struggling to understand the reason anyone would birth in a hospital or lay themselves at the mercy of unnecessary medical intervention, and the whole medicalised, and often fearful, birthing experience.

Still, what I was also beginning to recognise was that the pregnancy world is rife with fear. Even I was feeling it, in terms of the concern about miscarrying, let alone any of the other anxieties that pregnancy brings. At times, it was almost reassuring to feel sick, just to know that I was still pregnant! It's crazy really, as I'm not usually someone who experiences anxiety, so it was a bit of a shock how much this showed up during the pregnancy.

I have to say that those online pregnancy forums don't help matters and I would strongly encourage others to avoid them as much as they can. Perhaps, sometimes, they may be helpful, but on the whole, I think they just serve to further promote anxiety and prevent you checking in with your own wisdom and trusting in this.

I believe that we already know everything we need to know, and as mothers or mothers-to-be, our intuition is even stronger, certainly in respect of our children, be that Earth-side or in utero – I truly believe we know deep down if there's something wrong or not.

However, I found signing up to www.babycentre.co.uk was positively insightful, as you receive a weekly email, explaining the stage of development of the growing foetus, based on your estimated due date (see, it does have some positives I guess!). I found this helped me to connect more fully with the bean and also helped me to learn a little more about foetal development and the changes experienced by women at various stages of gestation.

I supplemented this with "week by week" yoga in a pregnancy book called *Yoga of Pregnancy Week by Week* by Mel Campbell (which had been recommended by one of the yoga teachers in Chiang Mai, who had strangely and quite by chance been on a retreat with me in Bali a few years earlier), where the author details the developmental stages, and complements this with yoga poses to support that particular gestation period.

Life continued much as usual over the coming weeks, with the sickness finally easing – thank the Goddess of the Moon – and by 16 weeks, it stopped altogether. Phew. It was like a switch being switched off; all of a sudden, it just went. In addition, I started to have more energy and felt like a normal human being again, albeit with an expanding waistline – it was such a relief! I think the trouble with morning sickness is you have no idea, especially that first time, when it will ease, and you can't help feeling a little bit anxious that it may continue the whole of the pregnancy – thankfully, not in my case!

Chapter 14
The 20-Week Scan and Placenta Previa

It wasn't long after the morning sickness eased that I felt my first fluttering. It was the strangest feeling, because it was ever so gentle, yet strong enough to catch my attention. You could easily have mistaken it for trapped wind, but the more it happened, the more I came to recognise that it was the baby moving inside me. Quite amazing!

By 19 weeks, I was feeling much more my usual self, to the extent that I even toasted my 38th birthday with a glass of champagne – never has champagne tasted so good! Up until that point, the mere thought of wine and champagne had been enough to turn my stomach, but now the sickness had eased, my taste buds were back to normal again. I also had a lot more energy, so I didn't have to crash into bed early each evening.

Ups and Downs

I was jubilant to be pregnant, although I'd come to realise that being pregnant didn't necessarily mean that I was constantly happy, as I may have once imagined. That was another lesson. I had spent so much of my adult life longing to meet the man with whom I could have a family that I felt my happiness depended on it. I'd searched the world twice over and spent a lot of time praying to the angels for this dream to come true.

I lost track of the number of conversations I'd had with my best friends about us finding our respective Mr Rights, and about the children we would one day have (one of those friends ended up with Mr Wright, incidentally – oh, how we chuckle about this!). I'd also lost track of the number of failed relationships we'd had between us in our search for "the one". It wasn't necessarily that we weren't happy with our lot, but we figured it would make us and our lives complete to have the "ideal" partner and our child in it.

And now, here I was, pregnant and with a loving partner, and yes, there was a certain feeling of completeness that came with that, but it didn't mean that I was constantly happy. There were days when I was very happy and incredibly joyous about the new life growing inside me, but equally, there were days when I felt out of sorts and a little miserable, and I found myself praying to the angels for guidance.

It reminded me that our state of happiness and sense of wellbeing is not dependent on anyone or anything else, but on our state of mind and our perspective. After all, we choose which thoughts we give our attention to. So, even pregnant, I still had my moments. Plus, I may well have realised the dream of meeting my partner and becoming pregnant, but now, I dreamt of a home vaginal birth – there was always another dream, something else to work towards.

The truth is, I thought that a vaginal homebirth was the only way I was going to experience spirituality in birth. I had this image in my head of me birthing on my own in the darkness of the bathroom, all primal and earthy. I expected to drop my awareness deep into my body and into the sensation of the pain I would inevitably be experiencing, so that I could gain insight into the very essence of life and the birthing process. In so doing, I imagined a spiritual awakening, a journey into the light, and a state of enlightenment.

E wasn't so sure about this homebirth malarkey. Understandably, he wasn't particularly bothered about my need for spiritual awakening; he was more concerned about the health of the baby and he or she arriving Earth-side safely. I was concerned about this too, but it wasn't my only consideration. I was adamant that the only way I would experience what I wanted to experience was in the home environment. I certainly had no intention of birthing in a hospital, as I wanted zero intervention.

Little did I realise how much I was setting myself up for a fall. I figured I was being all-spiritual and open-minded about birth, but now I look back, this was farthest from the truth. I was, in fact, incredibly close-minded and judgemental. I just couldn't understand the reason women would choose to birth in a hospital, and I certainly couldn't get my head around them choosing to have a caesarean section, or induction, and would be a little vocal about this at times.

20-WEEK SCAN

A week or so after my birthday, we had an appointment for the 20-week scan. As the date approached, I became increasingly anxious and short-tempered. It was ridiculous really, but I couldn't help myself. I felt on edge and no amount of praying to the angels or Goddess of the Moon was easing this. I certainly couldn't sit still to meditate, and I was distracted in my yoga practice too. Fear had taken hold and I couldn't seem to shift this.

The same sonographer who had undertaken our 12-week scan, and her colleague, who was undertaking some training with her, greeted us. This scan is carried out in the same way as the 12-week dating scan, with gel on my tummy, and the sonographer passing the ultrasound device backwards and forwards over my skin. I proudly bared my just visible baby bump and lay back on the bed, with E sitting beside me.

The 20-week scan looks in detail at the baby's bones, heart, brain, spinal cord, face, kidneys and abdomen, and allows the sonographer to look for physical abnormalities in the baby and specifically, for 11 conditions, some of which are very rare. In most cases, the scan will show that the baby appears to be developing normally, but sometimes, the sonographer will find or suspect a problem – some problems can be seen more clearly than others.

There is also the opportunity during this scan to discover the sex of the baby, although this isn't the intention of the scan per se, and there is no certainty that it will be 100% accurate. I've known two couples who were told at the

20-week scan that they were carrying girls, only to end up with boys upon delivery, causing quite a shock and a little adjustment, certainly in terms of pink-themed nurseries and pink clothes!

We didn't want to know the sex of the baby and made sure that the sonographers were aware of this. This didn't stop me being curious, however, especially as the image of the baby was so clear on the screen. It was amazing really. Here was our little bean, visible to the naked eye, wriggling around and doing his/her thing, and looking like a proper baby. It was very exciting.

The sonographer guided us through the process, as she carefully checked the baby's organs, and took the necessary measurements required by this scan to determine the size of the baby and check everything looked well. However, she was concerned about the positioning of my placenta, which was still lying low in my uterus. For training purposes, her male colleague, had a look too, and fortunately, the baby appeared fine and no obvious abnormalities were found.

PLACENTA PREVIA

I'd already researched this a little and had read that one of the most common problems spotted at the 20-week ultrasound is placenta previa. The placenta is the pancake-shaped organ, normally located near the top of the uterus, which supplies the baby with nutrients through the umbilical cord. Placenta previa is where the placenta gets too near to, or actually covers, some, or all, of the cervix.

It's a potentially dangerous condition because, if the placenta covers the cervix, it blocks the baby's way out, meaning a caesarean section is required to deliver the baby. More seriously, as the cervix dilates towards the end of pregnancy, the placenta can be torn and bleed, which can be life-threatening to mother and baby.

Complete or partial placenta previa, where the placenta covers at least a quarter, or even all of the cervix, occurs in around 1 in 200 pregnancies, and requires careful monitoring by a doctor. More common is a marginal placenta previa, where the placenta is close by, or touching the cervix, but not actually covering it.

At 20 weeks, when the placenta is relatively large, compared to the size of the uterus, many women appear to have placenta previa. However, as the uterus grows, the placenta moves further away from the cervix, and by the time they have another scan, 90% of women with marginal placenta previa at 20 weeks will likely be given the all-clear and be able to try for a vaginal birth.

Sadly, it looked unlikely that I would be in that 90%, as my placenta appeared to be completely covering the cervix. This meant I had to have yet another internal vaginal examination so that the sonographer could be absolutely certain of this. It wasn't quite what I had in mind that morning, and I was slightly daunted by the fact there were two sonographers present, one of whom was an unknown male, but one does what one has to do in the circumstances.

Much to my utter dismay, the vaginal scan revealed my fears; I had complete placenta previa and would most likely have to have a caesarean birth. The placenta was completely covering the cervix and in such a way that it was very unlikely it was going to move from this position. I knew that it wasn't going to move; I could feel it in my heart, and no amount of people telling me it would, or praying to the angels and the Goddess of the Moon, was going to change this. It was my fate.

Clearly, there were still lessons to be learned on this quest to procreate and become a mum. Going through IVF was not enough. And in many respects, looking back, I can see clearly the potential blessings in the curse. But back then, I was absolutely bereft and it was all I could do to hold it together in the scanning room as the sonographer told me that I would be referred to a specialist and that I should immediately telephone the hospital if I started to bleed.

Once outside the hospital building, I burst into tears. Poor E had no idea what was going on; as far as he was concerned, the baby was OK, so why was I crying? And that was the point I missed. Of course, I was delighted that the baby was healthy, but if I'm honest, I took that for granted. I hadn't anticipated a problem with the baby, and perhaps I wasn't as grateful as I should have been.

All I cared about in that moment was that I was going to have little choice but to have a caesarean section. The baby was going to enter the world in the completely opposite way to the one I had intended, namely now early, in a theatre, with lights and noise, and drugs and strangers. This was absolutely not how it was meant to be. I wanted spiritual music and candles, the darkness of the bathroom, and the opportunity to truly go within, birth without fear, and have a spiritual experience.

I had a lot to learn.

The Goddess of the Moon was dancing, but I most definitely wasn't dancing with her.

I telephoned my parents from the car and burst into tears all over again. They were concerned something was wrong with the baby and were relieved when they found out the problem was with my placenta instead. They tried to help me realise that I should be feeling relieved, not distraught. But I just couldn't see beyond the caesarean section. It was like a neon light in my mind flashing: "*caesarean section, caesarean section, caesarean section*".

I was angry, very angry. It just didn't seem fair. What was the Universe playing at? Not only had I had to have a clinical conception (albeit conscious, but it took me a while to recognise this), but now, here I was, going to have to have a clinical birth too. Plus, there was now an increased chance of painless vaginal bleeding during the third trimester and, with that, the risk of being hospitalised.

The bleeding happens when the cervix begins to thin out or open up (even a little), which disrupts the blood vessels in the area. What would happen after this would depend on the stage of pregnancy, the heaviness of the bleeding, and how the baby and I were doing. If the baby was still premature, he or she would be delivered immediately if the conditions warranted it, or if the bleeding was so heavy that it didn't stop.

Otherwise, I would be watched in the hospital until the bleeding stopped. If the baby was less than 34 weeks' gestation, I would be given steroids to speed up the baby's lung development and to prevent other complications in case he or she ended up being delivered prematurely. If the bleeding stopped and I remained free of bleeding for at least a couple of days then I would probably be sent home (it's likely that the bleeding would start up again at some point and, if that happened, then I would need to return to the hospital immediately).

However, if both of us continued to do well and the baby didn't need to be delivered right away, then a caesarean section would be scheduled at around 37 weeks, unless there was a reason to intervene earlier. When making the decision, the medical staff would need to weigh up the benefit of giving the baby extra time to mature, against the risk of waiting, with the possibility of facing an episode of heavy bleeding and the need for an emergency caesarean section.

In addition, after a baby is delivered by caesarean section, the obstetrician delivers the placenta and the mother is given medication to encourage the uterus to contract, which helps stop the bleeding from the area where the placenta was implanted. However, with placenta previa, the placenta is implanted in the lower part of the uterus, which doesn't contract as well as the upper part, so the contractions aren't as effective at stopping the bleeding. This may result in heavy bleeding and the need for a blood transfusion.

Also, women who have placenta previa are more likely to have a placenta that has implanted too deeply and that doesn't separate easily at delivery. This is called placenta accreta, which can cause massive bleeding and the need for multiple blood transfusions at delivery. It can be life-threatening and may require a hysterectomy to control the bleeding.

Finally, if you need to deliver before term, there is a risk that the baby will suffer complications from premature birth – such as breathing problems, low birth weight, and the need for neo-natal care. It was not ideal, certainly not what one would choose, and it brought with it not only the anger and frustration, but a huge amount of fear too.

Once I calmed down and accepted my reality (as much as I ever truly accepted it), I realised that I needed to do what I could to limit the chances of bleeding. I absolutely didn't want to end up hospitalised, and I had no intention of the baby arriving early. I had read far too much about the implications of premature delivery on a baby's gut and lung development, and the resulting effect this would have on their overall health and wellbeing, and I didn't want this for my baby.

I resolved, therefore, that my baby was *not* going to be delivered early. I was going to make it my mission to carry on life as usual and do what I could (intuitively) to ensure I didn't bleed. I was still very angry – and would be for a further three years – but I came to recognise that this condition presented me with yet another opportunity to drop deeper into my spiritual practice and listen, being guided by my body and the messages it was conveying to me.

Chapter 15
Yoga and Placenta Previa

Since discovering the holistic approach to healing and wellbeing years earlier, I had become increasingly resistant to the allopathic world. I rarely needed to see the doctor, and tried to take the natural approach at every opportunity, embracing the concept of healing thyself. I have always felt that there is an emotional/mental/spiritual perspective to any illness, and no amount of pharmaceutical drugs will resolve this without also making changes to our lifestyle and way of thinking etc.

So the fact I was now under the care of the allopathic world of specialists didn't fill me with much joy and, while I had little choice, I was resistant. I was so angry about the placenta previa, and while I appreciated that in the past, without scans and specialists, I would most certainly die at childbirth and probably the baby would die too, I couldn't truly open my heart to the care being provided.

I was still very much caught in the "us/them" world, which, when I reflect back, is laughable. As I mentioned earlier, there I was, trying to be an open-minded, non-judgemental yoga teacher and holistic practitioner, and yet, I was being exactly the opposite – close-minded and judgmental. I could only see "my way" and felt that any other way lacked the spirit of birth.

Unconsciously, I also felt I knew best and I was disapproving of anyone else's perspective. I was sick of people telling me it was all about the safety and wellbeing of the baby. "What about me?" I wanted to say to them. "Don't I get a say in this? What about my dreams, what about the spiritual homebirth and the orgasmic birthing and spiritual insights and awakenings that a vaginal birth can bring?"

But the thing is, with placenta previa, you don't get a say in anything as it's a life-threatening condition, and that is what frustrated me. I had no choice and I blamed anyone I could for this. I felt cheated of my dream and I loathed the fact that the allopathic world was telling me that the baby needed to be delivered early, and that due to my condition, there wouldn't be the opportunity for delayed cord clamping. It was infuriating.

Admittedly, while it would've been easy to lose heart and get awfully infuriated with the Universe and the angels, this whole sorry situation encouraged me to drop deeper into my spiritual practice to maintain my grounding. There were moments, of course, when I did get thoroughly depressed, and I felt that the Universe and the angels had it in for me, but actually, this was a necessary part of the process, and a surrendering often accompanied this.

In practice, what this meant is that I reached the end of my tether and broke down in tears, sobbing on my yoga mat until there were no more tears to sob, and praying for help from the angels. I was done with trying to control things (which is an illusion anyway), and was passing it on to the powers that be, and in so doing, there was often a form of awakening and with that some peace – it was like the old had to crumble to make way for the new.

A NEW FORM OF PREGNANCY YOGA

Crying on my yoga mat was a good start, and from there, I resolved to figure out a yoga practice that would help to keep the baby inside me for as long as possible. This meant practicing in the completely opposite way to the usual pregnancy yoga sequencing, which aims to prepare the body for birthing vaginally and opening everything up accordingly. It was time to put the books aside and go within again.

I am a qualified pregnancy yoga teacher with a solid understanding of how to teach and practice yoga to support a pregnancy and prepare for birth. However, my training also centred on preparing women for a vaginal delivery, and while we did address some of the common pregnancy complications, such as symphysis pubis dysfunction, we did not study placenta previa.

I researched '*yoga for placenta previa*' on the Internet, but found very little. I suspect no one really wants to take responsibility for advising women what they should or shouldn't practice, as there is such a huge risk of bleeding with this condition. In addition, many women are told to avoid exercise and others are put on bed rest for the duration of their pregnancy.

I quickly realised that I was going to have to figure this one out for myself, and practice intuitively. This is how yoga should be practiced ideally, aimed specifically at the individual, depending on what is going on for them at any one time. Of course, there are generalisations and the energies of alignment to consider, but every body (quite literally) is different, and in an ideal world, yoga should be adapted, and have the flexibility, to suit the individual student's needs.

Once again, the Universe had provided me with a further opportunity to deepen my experience of yoga, not that I realised the blessing in the curse at the time. I'd invited the Goddess of the Moon into my life, so I shouldn't have been surprised. She was dancing and weaving her magic in my life, but I was so caught up in it, I couldn't see her light.

ANGER

I was angry about my diagnosis and agonised over whether I had caused it. Ordinarily, during the first trimester, one is encouraged to ease off from all physical activity, including yoga, due to the higher risk of miscarriage that this trimester brings. Certainly, I never knowingly accept pregnant ladies into my class before 12 weeks. However, I paid little attention to this and carried on as usual, depending upon how sick and tired I was feeling.

Often, the yoga practice would ease my nausea and give me a little extra energy. I found backbends helpful with this, and twists, although I was mindful of the extent to which

I took these. The cells are multiplying at a massive rate during this period, and I tried to practice regular Yoga Nidra to rest and support this process. I attempted to meditate daily too, although this became increasingly tricky, as my mind would be so easily distracted by the nausea.

I like Vedic chanting, but during the first trimester, I found that I couldn't do this as it made me feel very sick. I suspect the energy was too strong for the sensitivity of the developing cells within me, and it was only later in the pregnancy that I was able to chant again. I was keen to do all I could, energetically, to bathe the growing baby with as much light energy as possible and I made sure to play uplifting music during my practice.

I researched the potential causes of placenta previa, but no mention was made of exercise. Instead, research suggests that a pregnant woman is more likely to have this condition if she has had previous pregnancies, a previous caesarean section, uterine scars, is carrying twins or more, is a smoker, uses cocaine and/or is an older mother. I certainly ticked the older mother box, but that aside, none of these other causes resonated with me, and I finally let myself off the hook and concluded that it was just meant to be that way.

During the second trimester (13 to 28 weeks), when my normal energy levels returned again, I found movement absolutely essential in helping to keep my mind as strong as my body. This became even more important when I discovered that I had placenta previa, especially as I was so irritated in those earlier days, and welcomed my practice as an opportunity to work through my frustration and try to stay grounded.

It was a tough period. The pregnancy hormones alone left me tearful and angry at times, and this was now compounded by the recent diagnosis. Up until that point, E had never seen me having an anger outburst, and to be honest, I naively thought I'd worked through all my anger issues during years of yoga, Reiki and other healing work. I was wrong, and I was as surprised as E. Clearly, pregnancy was bringing up a whole other level of stuff that needed expression.

It didn't help that I knew that anger was a waste of energy. One of the Reiki principles is "just for today, do not anger". The reason being that anger is a destructive emotion when expressed inappropriately and can create disharmony in the body. That said, I was also aware that it can be a powerful motivator for change, provided you are consciously aware of your reactions and take charge of your emotions.

Essentially, it comes down to expectation and the need to let go of it. Whether the expectations are those of other people or situations, it doesn't matter. We get angry when our expectations are not met, so the idea is that we let go of expectations, just for today, and see each situation as it is right now. Needless to say, I was struggling with this, and it didn't help that I should have known better.

So I took to my mat with extra vigour. I continued with my vinyasa practice and paid little attention to the usual guidelines as I moved intuitively. For me, it felt great to practice deep backbends, as they energised me, and helped to relieve the strange sensation of my stretching skin. I also continued inverting, as I knew I was going to be having a caesarean section, so I didn't need to concern myself with the positioning of the baby and thus, compromise a vaginal birth.

Intuitively, it felt necessary to avoid the poses that women are generally encouraged to practice during pregnancy, the ones that help to prepare the body for a vaginal birth. Instead, I felt that I needed to do all I could to keep this baby inside me and to reduce any pressure on the placenta, nestled, as it was, snuggly over the cervix.

This meant no wide-legged seated or standing poses and no squatting. Instead, I ended up practicing poses such as Gomukhasana (Cow's face), Virasana (Hero's pose) and Garudasana (Eagle pose), which helped to draw everything in. I also continued with the backbends, arm balances and the inversions right up until the end of the pregnancy, as these felt supportive to the pregnancy.

The amazing thing was, during the latter part of the second and even into the third trimester (29-40 weeks), my body made it extremely clear to me which poses to practice and which to avoid. Not only did the bump make it obvious that poses on the tummy and closed twists should be absolutely avoided, but also I started experiencing increasing sacroiliac pain.

This is not uncommon in pregnancy, and certainly, there is a prevalence of this condition amongst flexible female yoga practitioners. During pregnancy, the body produces a hormone called relaxin, which softens the ligaments and, in theory, helps the baby to pass more easily through the pelvis during birth. This means that the joints can become more mobile during pregnancy and this can cause all sorts of problems, especially for the sacroiliac joint.

Interestingly, the pain around that joint was aggravated by all the poses that I had already felt I should avoid during my pregnancy. It was genius. My body was absolutely leading the way, and I had no choice but to listen. It was deeply empowering to recognise that my body knew what was best for it, in such a profound way.

It was for this reason that I made sure to again prioritise a daily 20-minute meditation practice and enjoy regular Yoga Nidra during my pregnancy. There is no doubt that both my mind and body benefitted immensely from these practices and helped me to stay strong, mentally and physically. Pregnancy provided me with an enormous opportunity to hear, listen to, honour and respect my body in a way I hadn't done previously.

Pregnancy also helped to significantly shift my awareness and experience of yoga, albeit not in the way I had imagined, and it took me a few years to realise this. I had been so keen to embody the teachings of my pregnancy yoga training, that there was a part of me that felt cheated that I wasn't able to use yoga to prepare for a vaginal birth, as I'd seen so many others do and use it to their benefit too.

ANITA'S INFLUENCE

During my second trimester, I started attending the weekly pregnancy yoga class, taught by my doula and friend, Anita.

Initially, in the earlier days, when I didn't have a bump, I found these classes challenging, simply because I wasn't used to practicing so slowly and gently. But as the pregnancy progressed, I absolutely loved them, and they became the highlight of my week, two hours every Sunday evening to truly indulge in the pregnancy.

Anita created a very sacred and special space with a beautiful altar and candles brightening the room, and calming music playing in the background, so that you couldn't help but feel nourished and nurtured. It was a good balancer for me to be able to practice a gentler and more feminine approach to yoga movement, to complement my more active and yang home practice. It was also a real treat to be guided by someone else, and especially someone as passionate about pregnancy and birth as Anita.

I loved sharing the space with other pregnant ladies, as we all took the opportunity to connect with our growing babies. I loved feeling the energy of the baby inside me and I was fascinated by how this shifted throughout the pregnancy, so that it became denser and more attuned to my own energy, or me to the baby's energy perhaps.

It seemed to me that the baby had come into the world, in utero then, with its own energy field (which I couldn't penetrate) and energetic disposition. This isn't to say that my own energy work, and indeed my thoughts and emotions, wouldn't impact on it in some way; I believe they do, and there is research to substantiate this, but more so that the baby was clearly its own person from the outset and I was his/her nourishing vessel. Thus, I wanted to do all I could to ensure a loving and nurturing environment for his/her growth.

This was a tricky awareness for me at times, because I was keen to do all I could to ensure that the baby didn't absorb the anger and frustration I felt towards the placenta previa. And yet, I struggled at times with this, because it then became easy to beat myself up about it! I was also very aware that I didn't want the baby to absorb the fear I felt towards the caesarean section, but try as I might, it was difficult not to become consumed with this.

So, my practice became important to me, energetically and emotionally too, to try to shift my thinking and immerse the baby in lovely yogic and feminine energy. Anita's classes helped considerably with this, as they gave me the space to just be with my baby and deepen my connection to him/her in utero. He or she was certainly an active baby and responded immediately to me getting on my mat or placing my hands on my bump to channel Reiki.

During the pregnancy yoga classes, Anita was keen to share with us breathing techniques and visualisations, which may assist us during the birth (regardless of the nature of the birth). The combination of these and the guided relaxations left me feeling incredibly calm and nourished by the end of the sessions. The only trouble was that towards the end of the pregnancy, when I knew with certainty that I was having a caesarean section (I had been praying for a miracle, just in case!), I switched off from the preparation for birth bit.

It didn't seem important to me to know how to breathe through contractions or how to use the visualisations to manage my pain, as I wouldn't be contracting or experiencing the pain that accompanies this. There was a part of me that was desperately sad about this and while I went through the motions, my mind was often elsewhere, running through lists of what I needed to do that week, as my life certainly hadn't slowed down.

If anything, I became busier. It was a coping mechanism, I realise, to keep myself occupied so I wouldn't think too much about the impending birth and the caesarean section. It is perhaps no surprise that in practicing a yang style of yoga daily, I was very yang in my approach to life, just getting on with it, helped by the fact that my workload in the office was incredibly demanding at the time.

Anita would read the most beautiful quotes during her yoga classes, which talked about the surrendering and letting go that pregnancy and birth encouraged. While I understood this intellectually, I didn't really know what she meant in practice, and figured this only really applied to a vaginal birth.

I certainly wasn't doing any surrendering and letting go, quite the opposite in fact, I was holding on for dear life. I didn't want to bleed, I didn't want to have the baby earlier than necessary, and I was still resistant to the idea of the caesarean birth.

While my connection to the Goddess of the Moon in all her divine, feminine beauty deepened during pregnancy, so that I would bathe in her 28-day light and give thanks and pray to her, I still didn't yet know what it meant to dance with her.

Anita leads regular wise women workshops too, and I was fortunate to attend one of these sessions during the latter part of my pregnancy. Together, we belly danced and moved our bodies, swaying and circling and enjoying the movement that resonates with the feminine aspect of ourselves on a very deep level. We drew labyrinths and doodled on stones, and I found this opportunity for creative expression hugely enlightening.

I shall always be eternally grateful to Anita for her love and the energy she put into these sessions, to help us recognise a part of ourselves that we may not have acknowledged previously. Here we were, all pregnant ladies, embodying both the energy of creation in its most primitive sense and spirit in its purest expression. And these wise women sessions helped me to truly tap into the energy of this; the power of the divine feminine.

This is not to say that the divine feminine is only present in pregnancy, however. She is present in our everyday life experience, regardless of the stage of life, whether maiden, mother, crone or otherwise. It took me a long time to recognise this, and to know it as an absolute truth within me. And this wise women workshop, which created a collective feminine energy that I had not experienced previously, laid a seed for the future direction that my life and my yoga practice would take.

Still, as the birth approached and I sat with the energy growing inside me, I had to dig very deep into my practice, to overcome the increasing dread I felt about the birth. It was for this reason that I kept things active right up until the end, to the extent that at 29 weeks pregnant, I attended a workshop in London with Cyndi Lee, a truly inspiring American teacher, with a sign-off from my doctor for travel off-island.

I continued teaching right up until I was 36 weeks pregnant too. This wasn't right or wrong and certainly not an indication of what others should do, just this felt right for me during that pregnancy. It gave me a purpose and took my mind away from what was, inevitably, to come. It unsettled one of the male students in particular though, as each week my bump grew bigger, and he was worried I may go into labour during a class!

The baby was breech in the end. Whether this was due to the positioning of my pelvis, or the placenta previa, or me inverting my body throughout my pregnancy, I shall never know.

But in practicing in the way that my body guided, I did not bleed once during my pregnancy, and I didn't have to go on bed rest or avoid strenuous activity, and the baby didn't arrive earlier than planned either. It could just have been luck, but I like to believe it was the yoga!

CHAPTER 16

The Trials and Tribulations of Pregnancy

I absolutely loved being pregnant; it had felt like a long time in coming, and I was keen to enjoy every part of it. That's not to say it was without its challenges, not at all. Pregnancy is rife with them, at least that's my experience, but it was all a novelty to me that first time.

CHALLENGES

The first trimester was certainly tough going – the morning sickness, the inherent tiredness and the miscarriage scare. So too the need to pee all the time. It was crazy how often I needed to go to the toilet during the night, sometimes as much as six times! I didn't realise initially that this need to pee is often one of the first signs of pregnancy, no one had mentioned that to me, but then no one had mentioned much to me about pregnancy, beyond the morning sickness.

This excessive need to pee seemed to be an on/off theme throughout the pregnancy, depending on the hormonal changes taking place at any one time, and the positioning of the baby in the growing uterus, which at times, pressed on the bladder. The peeing at night thing got so ridiculous that I even stopped drinking water in the early evening and tried to reduce my consumption of high-water content vegetables and salads, as I was convinced this was compounding the situation, but it seemed to make little difference.

The peeing thing certainly was my main concern when it came to our festival camping that summer too. It wasn't so bad at the Sark Folk Festival, as we were camping in a field and I could easily pee to the side of the field without disturbing anyone else. It's actually rather pleasant peeing outside in the darkness of the night, with the stars above and the sound of the sea in the distance.

The WOMAD festival was a bit trickier. The campsite was rammed with tents so I took along a bucket and used that in the tent during the night instead. There was no way I was traipsing all the way to the communal toilets and risking tripping over tent pegs and ropes in the process. It felt a tad awkward the next morning, going to empty my bucket, but we were up earlier than most, as I certainly wasn't partying late into the night!

There was a respite during the second trimester, when the peeing was replaced with indigestion and heartburn. The indigestion is partly caused by hormonal changes, and in later pregnancy, by the growing uterus pressing on the stomach. Heartburn, on the other hand, is caused by stomach acid passing from the stomach into the oesophagus and is really rather debilitating.

The heartburn certainly challenged me because it didn't seem to matter how healthily I ate. I'd still end up with this horrible burning sensation in my throat. I finally figured out that apples, pitta bread and eating my lunch at my desk aggravated it, so I avoided that. The only way I could ever seem to relieve it was by chewing gum or, if that didn't work, taking Gaviscon. Neither options were ideal, but it got to the point where I didn't care too much, and I was almost overdosing on Gaviscon at times, anything to feel some relief.

There were nights where I had to try and sleep virtually upright, supported by a whole heap of pillows, to ease the burning sensation in my throat. I had to adjust my yoga practice too, and ensure I didn't eat for a good while before getting onto my mat. E got sick of hearing me moaning about it, but it's one of those things that unless you've experienced it, you don't realise how unbearable it can be, especially when it happens day in and day out, and you feel powerless to change it.

Then, all of a sudden, the heartburn disappeared, and I became consumed by the discomfort of constipation instead.

Like most, I loathe being constipated, as it makes me feel so yucky, and I have always tried to do what I can, from a diet and lifestyle perspective, to support my digestive system and ensure regular bowel movement. I drank lots of water, ate short grain brown rice, consumed soaked linseeds, took probiotics, and practiced yoga poses, which are meant to ease constipation, but none of these approaches seemed to make any difference.

The trouble is, during pregnancy, you experience an increase in the hormone progesterone, which relaxes the smooth muscles throughout the body, including the digestive tract. This means that food passes through the intestines more slowly. This can be compounded later on in the pregnancy by the pressure of the growing uterus on the rectum. Iron supplements, particularly in high doses, can often make constipation worse, which was one reason I wanted to avoid them if I could.

But alas not. My iron levels dipped during the pregnancy, probably a result of my vegetarian diet, and also the fact the baby takes whatever minerals and vitamins it needs from the mother, often leaving her with diminished supplies. I was prescribed iron tablets, but these made me feel horrible, so I stopped taking them and tried to do what I could through my diet to increase my iron levels instead. I supplemented with iron water and Floradix liquid iron, but I was never sure these were effective.

It wasn't all grey clouds though, there were lots of silver linings too. These conditions were all very annoying but were hugely overridden by the joy of being pregnant in the first place. Here I was, growing a real life human being inside of me; it was both magical and mysterious. I'm astounded to this day that my body knew how to do this without me giving it any thought and without me having to truly get involved in the process – well, beyond the conception and eating well. That in itself is nothing short of a miracle!

Throughout my pregnancy, I continued with my usual workload, teaching yoga, channelling Reiki, and working in the office part-time. In addition to trying to practice regular

Yoga Nidra, I also tried to make an effort to rest during the day, but resting has never come easily to me, and I was grateful for the summer sun, as it encouraged me to lie down and bathe in it. I had to be careful though, because skin becomes more sensitive to the sun during pregnancy due to rising hormone levels, and is at greater risk of burning.

I found swimming invaluable while I was pregnant. During the summer, I made the most of sea swimming, something that we do all year around anyway, but that became essential while pregnant, to cool down and take the weight off. It's an exceptional leveller, as you cannot help but feel more grounded, energised and uplifted after being in the sea, especially at my favourite south coast bays, nestled by the stunning cliffs.

I swam in a swimming pool too to keep myself fit, and also to ease the strange sensation of the skin stretching to accommodate the growing baby. I have scar tissue from surgery many years ago now, when my gallbladder was removed, and the expanding bump had to stretch through this. At times, it felt extremely uncomfortable, like the skin itself would split (to the extent I thought maybe I should see a doctor), and swimming seemed to be the only thing to ease this.

While the discomfort of the stretching skin finally eased, I then experienced times where the skin over my tummy would feel really itchy and I'd find myself scratching incessantly. I massaged organic Vitamin E oil onto my tummy each night, which I believe helped to keep the skin supple and prevented stretch marks forming during the pregnancy. It's incredible that the skin can stretch as it does and contract back again afterwards.

As my stomach grew, I became increasingly aware of the baby's movements. It's remarkable that you get to feel the baby moving inside you, and it freaked E out. My mum, on the other hand, loved putting her hand on my tummy and channelling Reiki, and feeling her grandchild kick. It was an active baby and there was certainly a lot of kicking at all times of day and night.

Sometimes, it felt that I had a foot wedged up in my diaphragm, so it made it difficult and uncomfortable to breathe, and other times, it was back to the pressure in my bladder as the baby pressed down on it. I loved watching my tummy move; this was particularly obvious in the bath, but often when I was sunbathing too. He or she responded to Reiki almost immediately and it was a constant source of comfort to be able to feel the baby move so easily, so that I knew it was literally alive and kicking.

Special treatment

What astounded me most was all the attention I received while pregnant, and the fact that the general public treat you so differently. Complete strangers would remark on the bump and ask after my health and wellbeing, as well as enquiring into my due date and the sex of the baby – and often telling me what sex they thought the baby would be on account of the shape of my bump. It was quite extraordinary and rather entertaining at times too.

Consequently, I felt supported and cared for in a way that I have never felt previously. Doors were held open, chairs were provided, people would offer to carry things for me – my students were great, someone would always meet me when I arrived at class to help carry things up the stairs, and in the office, the boys wouldn't even let me empty the shredding bins – and generally, people were rather lovely to me. It was marvellous and made me consider how wonderful the world would be if we were all treated with such courtesy and compassion every day!

I received lots of attention from the medical world too. Initially, of course, there was the IVF and the early pregnancy scans this brought with it, then the miscarriage scare and the additional scan for this, and then the placenta previa. This meant yet more scans and appointments with the specialist to discuss the birth and what might happen if I began bleeding before then. And, of course, there were appointments with the midwife (it wasn't always the same one), which increased in frequency as the pregnancy progressed.

I continued to channel Reiki to myself, as much as I could, and especially onto the growing baby. This was certainly going to be a Reiki baby and I was excited about what this might mean in terms of future behaviour and sensitivity to energy etc. Although I wasn't sure how much of that would be due to the Reiki or to genetic and energetic disposition, let alone past-life experience and Akashic records.

I also received Reiki regularly from a fellow Reiki practitioner, especially as the birth date approached. I felt that the Reiki helped to keep me on a relatively even keel during this unsettling time and encouraged rest and healing too. I always felt so much better after a session, and truly believe that every pregnant lady should receive Reiki during her pregnancy. It's deeply relaxing, non-invasive, very gentle, and benefits both mother and baby.

What also helped was spending time in nature. I walked regularly through the lanes near our cottage, and out on the stunning cliffs, often with E in tow. I have fond memories of the time we spent together walking and often chatting about how our lives were about to change, and yet, neither of us really having any idea of the extent of that change. I don't know that you can ever appreciate the magnitude of the change for you until you've experienced it first-hand.

I'll never forget a conversation I had with my mum one day about how things might or might not change. We were out walking and chatting excitedly about life with the baby and about how I was going to manage my workload. I distinctly remember hearing myself say, "But it can't be that difficult, all babies do is sleep, feed and poo; I'll have plenty of time to work." She tried to manage my expectations but I was truly in denial.

BUYER BEWARE

By then, I'd bought a lot of the stuff that friends had suggested I might need when the baby arrived. It certainly was a lot.

E wasn't involved in this process, as I think it was all too much for him; life really was changing! We were fortunate that we bought most of our stuff second-hand from a family friend, which helped keep our costs down. You can get really carried away with all this and I now know that, actually, you need very little for a baby.

We bought brand new flat pack furniture for the baby's room, a wardrobe and drawers designed specifically for use in a nursery, as I felt the baby should have something new. I'll never make that mistake again. I thought I was being a wonderfully clever mummy, putting it all together one weekend all on my own, but the truth is, it wasn't much of an investment as its never worked properly and I've no idea why I thought I needed furniture like this, specifically designed for a baby, because certainly we had far too much baby stuff to fit into a diddy cupboard!

I initially made a mistake with pregnancy clothes too. Someone had told me to simply buy clothes in a bigger size, but in my opinion, this was rubbish advice. You can't beat the comfort of proper maternity clothes, and while it feels a waste of money to buy these for such a short period of time, it was well worth it, from my experience. I was lucky, as some clothes were donated to me, and to be honest, I just got used to wearing the same things all the time; it was no big deal.

Pregnancy is funny because sometimes, it seems to drag on – certainly, when I was suffering morning sickness or waiting anxiously for a scan. Then, at other times, you just want it to last forever – I'm thinking of the second trimester and lolling around on yoga mats, sunbeds and at festivals. And then, towards the end of the pregnancy, I got to a point where I was ready to get on with it and meet the new life growing inside of me.

Ordinarily, unless you have a planned caesarean section, you don't know when this first meeting might be, and there's lots of excited anticipation around this, not only for the expectant mother, but for family and friends too. I didn't get to experience this though, as I knew in advance the day the baby would be arriving, and I wasn't altogether happy about this.

I did not want the baby being dragged out of its cosy home without any warning, without it being ready, without it being squeezed through the birth canal and gaining the benefits of this – not least in releasing the hormone epinephrine, which clears fluids from the lungs and reduces the likelihood of respiratory issues, but also in exposing the baby to beneficial bacteria to reduce the chances of the baby developing asthma, food allergies and lactose intolerance in later life.

I didn't want the cord cut early, nor the baby to miss out on immediate skin to skin, and all the benefits that both these practises bring to the future health and wellbeing of the baby, and indeed me. I also didn't want to be in a position where I couldn't breastfeed the baby following the birth, and therefore, unintentionally create any bonding issues as a result of not being able to do this.

I didn't want to be in a hospital, I didn't want surgery, I didn't want to take drugs, especially antibiotics, which would destroy all the good bacteria in my gut, and potentially lead to all sorts of digestive issues, let alone mental and emotional issues too. I also didn't want to have to spend weeks recovering, not able to drive, not able to lift anything and not able to exercise or get on my mat. And nor did I want to feel like a failure because of all this.

So it was with a very heavy heart that I sat with E in the specialist's office as a date was agreed for the planned caesarean section. It was another one of those moments that I'll never forget. The specialist, a lovely man originally from South Africa, who is very passionate about birth, wanted to deliver the baby at approximately 38.5 weeks. With this awareness, he looked in his diary to figure out the date this would be, and whether there was any theatre availability. He concluded that 12th November would work very nicely for him; how did we feel about this?

Well, it was a rhetorical question really, and it struck me that a medical professional could choose the date to bring your baby Earth-side, depending on his work schedule and theatre availability, and with that, affect its horoscope and its future life path, depending upon the positioning of the planets on that day.

But there you go. The date was set. That was that. It would seem that rather than bringing a Sagittarius into the world, which would have been the case if the baby arrived on his/her due date, we would be bringing a Scorpio into the world instead. Now I just needed to make it until the date without any bleeding and without going into early labour, although I was adamant that this wouldn't happen.

The specialist was very kind and very excited about helping us to birth our baby safely. Before we left his office, he wanted to know whether we had any questions. Well no, not really, I was too busy trying to get my head around and accept the fact that the baby would be born at 38.5 weeks' gestation, a whole week and a half earlier than the "due" date. I believed that this "early" delivery would result in the baby having fragile lungs and a dodgy digestive system, and with that, a weak immune system and years of allergies ahead.

The specialist tried to allay my fears. He explained that at 37 weeks' gestation, a pregnancy is considered full-term, as the baby's lungs are understood to be fully developed and the baby's gut contains meconium – the sticky, green substance that forms the baby's first poo after birth. Also, while the immune system is still developing, the baby is considered to be able to survive perfectly well outside the womb without any need for special care.

That said, he was keen to allow the pregnancy to progress beyond 37 weeks, but was trying to balance that against the risk of me going into early labour and suffering blood loss as a result of the placenta previa. Thus, 38.5 weeks seemed a happy medium, not that I was particularly happy about any of it.

I certainly wasn't pleased either that my condition brought with it an increased risk of blood loss during the caesarean section, and with that, a potential blood transfusion. It certainly wasn't ideal, and I was upset about the prospect of this. I was keen to provide my own blood in advance, in case it was required, but sadly, this wasn't allowed. This frustrated me, and I was adamant that I didn't want to have to take on someone else's blood and energy, and prayed with renewed vigour for a safe birth.

PART 3

The Birth

Chapter 17
Preparing for the Birth

Keeping busy

A week after seeing the specialist, I went to see the anaesthetist. She explained that the caesarean section would be carried out with spinal anaesthesia, which involves a one-off injection in the lower spine that works quickly and gives sufficient anaesthesia for the whole operation. This would enable me to be conscious during the whole birth and for E to join me in theatre.

However, she did stress that there's always a risk that the spinal anaesthesia doesn't take properly and then a general anaesthetic would then be required. If this happened, E wouldn't be allowed into theatre, so neither of us would witness the birth. The whole concept of missing the birth filled me with huge fear. I'd known this happen to friends of mine, and it had taken them a long time to come to terms with it.

I was aware that the anaesthetist was under an obligation to inform me of the worst-case scenario, but I wish I hadn't known. It was totally irrational on my part, but I couldn't let this idea of missing the birth go. Not one single thing about the conception or the pregnancy had gone the way I intended and now I just had this horrible feeling that I wouldn't even get to see the baby arrive Earth-side.

Again, while I knew that I should be transmuting this feeling of fear into love instead, I was well and truly caught up in the negativity of it. My solar plexus, my navel centre then, was certainly not happy, and I could feel it gurgling as the anxiety crept in, and the big black hole of despair begin to open up again. My heart didn't stand a chance in keeping the love alive… the fear had set in.

So I kept busy. Being busy is most definitely what I do best, and now I had a good reason to keep busy, as it would help to distract me from the fear. Fortunately, an additional project at work presented itself at this time so ensured that I was very busy, right up until the end of the pregnancy.

Despite the need to be busy, at 36 weeks, I realised that it was time to ease up on teaching yoga and channelling Reiki. I was carrying my baby all out front, and my bump was beginning to get in the way – it was becoming increasingly challenging to demonstrate poses during yoga classes, and the students were concerned of an early delivery in the yoga space! This gave me additional time to focus on the office work instead.

I had decided that I would work right up until the day before the planned birth. My best friend from school, who had birthed four children by then, was keen to stress to me the need to take some time out to calm and relax myself ahead of the birth, but I was having none of it. I was only able to take 12 weeks' maternity leave as it was, and I felt that I wanted to save all of that time to spend with the baby, plus, I was just far too busy at work to leave any earlier than this.

As it was, I didn't know quite how I was going to get everything finished in time, and as only part of my role was being covered in my absence, I was well aware that I would need to keep abreast of things during my maternity leave. Knowing when I was likely to have the baby did then have its positives, in so much as enabling me to plan and manage my workload.

Looking back, I realise how desperately unprepared I was for the arrival of the baby and how much I was in denial about how my life would change. I'd become so wrapped up in the pregnancy and the birth that I hadn't really thought beyond this. I had overlooked the fact that the pregnancy, and indeed the birth, were all leading me to the ultimate dream, which had always been to have a baby.

That's not to belittle the experience of being pregnant; I loved it! It was insightful and beautiful, and I had grown rather attached to my bump. And while the birth was still an unknown quantity to me, I was aware that it can be a hugely empowering and beautiful experience; not only does it mark the transition from maidenhood to motherhood, but it also brings new life into the world. It's certainly a big deal.

But it had become nothing short of a huge drama in my life, and I was so caught up in it that I couldn't see the bigger picture. It was the baby that I had spent most of my life dreaming about having. Not the birth. Not the pregnancy. And yet, all I'd done for the past eight months was read books on pregnancy and birth, and not one single book on babies and how to care for them. We hadn't even joined the NCT classes as this wasn't really E's thing and I was teaching yoga every night so I didn't have the time.

I was also in complete denial about how having a baby would affect my working life. I just assumed that this would continue as usual. My parents had already kindly agreed to look after the baby while I was in the office and E would be able to look after him or her while I was teaching yoga and practicing Reiki. I just felt that my life would fairly much continue as usual, just with a little bit more organisation!

Getting prepared

D-day – or C-day really – loomed ahead of me, as I tried to get on top of my workload and do what I could mentally to prepare myself for the birth. I didn't feel there was anything to do physically, because it didn't feel like I was going to be doing much birthing – the baby was going to be birthed for me. This knowledge created a strange feeling, but by then, I'd stopped giving it too much thought. It's not that I'd accepted my fate, far from it, more that I tried not to think about it too much.

My home yoga practice was essential at this time, and I made sure to get on my mat every day. I was still practicing an active form of yoga, which is not generally encouraged by the pregnancy yoga books, but it felt right for me during this period. I was also attending the weekly pregnancy yoga classes with Anita right up until the weekend before the birth. The slow pace of these classes made much more sense to me now. My energy levels were not what they had been earlier on in the pregnancy, the bump was decidedly large, and my back often ached.

Not only that, but I couldn't get a good night's sleep on account of all the trips to the toilet, and the effort it took to find a comfortable sleeping position, propped up I was with a number of pillows. Everyone kept telling me to rest and get as much sleep as I could, which began to annoy me after a while, as I found it impossible to do either in this later stage of pregnancy. Still, I made the most of the opportunity to soak in a warm, lavender-infused bath, and I tried to get to bed early, even if it was just to read my book.

As C-day quickly approached, the frequency of the appointments with my midwife increased. By then, I was generally seeing the same midwife on every visit, although it was unlikely she'd be present at the birth. These were used to check my blood pressure, check for protein in my urine, listen to the baby's heartbeat, measure the size of my bump (to check baby was growing properly), and to check the positioning of the baby, which was still breech!

Fortunately, I didn't bleed, which was a relief. That's not to say I didn't spend much of the latter part of the pregnancy constantly concerned about bleeding. Any slight change in sensation of discharge found me dashing to the nearest toilet or to the nearest place where I could discretely check whether the discharge was blood. After the earlier miscarriage scare, I was paranoid about blood, and the placenta previa merely compounded this.

A few weeks before the planned birth, I was told that I needed to be on the ward by 7a.m. on the morning of the surgery, with the surgery itself scheduled for later that morning. It sounds silly but this incensed me. I didn't want to be in the hospital any longer than I needed to be, and I certainly didn't want to be getting up for 7a.m. to spend a few hours sitting around in the hospital, getting tired and increasingly anxious about the procedure.

I wanted to stay at home until the last moment and have time to practice yoga in an effort to centre and ground myself ahead of this most life-changing event. I spoke with my midwife to see if the time could be changed, but she was powerless to do anything about it. Before too long, the whole "time to go to the hospital" became something of a drama, because it made absolutely no sense to me, and it was one thing I felt that I should be able to control, because let's face it, I couldn't control anything else about the birth.

I had lost all control, and this really got to me. The Goddess of the Moon was dancing, and I still didn't know how to dance with her. I didn't know how to let go and surrender to it. I didn't know how to go with the flow because none of this flow was flowing the way I wanted it to.

Fortunately, my lovely doula, Anita, whose services were somewhat limited now by the medicalised nature of the birth, spoke to the Head of Midwifery and negotiated a later arrival time for me. It's sounds silly, but this made a huge difference to my mental state, and while I was still petrified about all the things that could go wrong about the birth itself, at least I had longer that morning at home to practice some yoga and centre myself.

The weekend prior to the birth, I tried to prepare myself as best I could, not least in terms of getting in the sea to ground myself (no wetsuit by the way, not sure you can get pregnancy ones in any event!), but also in preparing the cottage for the arrival of the baby and preparing my hospital bag. A friend, who had previously had a number of caesarean sections, helpfully suggested what I might need to help with this, post-op, in terms of clothing. I also made sure to stock up on pro-biotics and arnica.

I was still in some denial about what lay ahead. I had read nothing about caesarean birth and the implications of this post-partum, as I didn't want to experience any additional fear. And while on the one hand, I joked about taking my yoga mat with me into the hospital, I did exactly that, because I figured I would be able to practice post-op in the time that the baby was sleeping – how I laugh about this now!

I worked in the office until 5.30p.m. the night before the birth and continued working on my Blackberry later into the evening. It felt very surreal, knowing that I wouldn't be back in the office, well, not properly, for 12 weeks, and yet, mentally, still very much in the "work" zone, despite knowing I was going to meet my baby the next day. This wasn't how I imagined birth to be!

Sleep certainly didn't come easily that evening. I was excited about finally meeting our little bean Earth-side, but anxious too about the caesarean section, and whether I'd be able to breastfeed, and the fact our life would never again be the same. Of course, I wanted this change, I wouldn't have chosen to get pregnant otherwise, but the enormity of it was desperately challenging in that moment, and I knew E felt it too.

Fortunately, by then, his back had sorted itself out. Funnily enough, it had started to improve when we knew that I was not carrying twins. He was helped with his healing by the confidence of the doctor he was seeing, who encouraged him to exercise and get on with life as normal, and not be scared by the pain. It was a really insightful experience for both of us – we were just relieved that he didn't have to have surgery. Still, he was having twinges, now that the birth was soon upon us.

We'd been such free spirits for so much of our lives, more or less able to do what we wanted when we wanted, that we were both concerned, in our own ways, about how this would be affected with a baby in our lives too. Only time would tell, and for now, I was just grateful that I could begin the next day with a short practice on my mat to centre myself and a moment in the garden, in the cool and damp air, desperately trying to also ground myself, ahead of the hospital experience.

Chapter 18

The Caesarean Birth

There's no denying the fact that I was nothing short of terrified as we arrived at the hospital that gloomy November morning for the birth of our baby.

I'd barely slept the night before, and while I'd managed my much-needed early morning yoga practice, no amount of conscious breathing was really going to stop me feeling on edge.

I'd read extensively about "birthing without fear", yet here I was, feeling exactly the opposite. There was a certain finality to leaving the cottage that morning, as I knew that life would never be the same again. I was excited, of course, but also extremely nervous about the unknown and consumed by the anxiety of whether we'd have the chance to witness our baby being born.

We tried to stay jolly during the short drive to the hospital and onwards on the walk up to Loveridge Ward, the maternity unit at the Princess Elizabeth Hospital here in Guernsey, where I'd been born too. As requested, we arrived at the ward at 8a.m., which still seemed ridiculously early to me, especially as we then spent the next few hours sitting around, waiting for something to happen.

I was allocated a bed close to the central nurse's station, although the curtains were drawn around it so we had some privacy. There was nothing much we could do, aside from sit around and wait, me on the bed, responding to work emails on my Blackberry, and E attempting to read a magazine as he sat on a chair beside me, drinking tea. I was nil by mouth from midnight and desperate for a cup of tea!

It felt that there was an assumption we knew the routine of being here on the ward, but it was all new to us. We weren't familiar with the ward, nor the manner in which it was run. And while an initial midwife was allocated to us, she was quickly whisked away to an emergency and replaced with another one instead.

This second midwife had recently moved to Guernsey, so we chatted about life on the island, as I was keen to establish a relationship with someone who might be with us during such a life-changing event. She ran through the preliminaries for the caesarean section and handed me a gown, which I would need to wear to go down to theatre.

My friend had already warned me about the need to shave the upper part of my pubic hair, so I'd done that earlier in the morning, saving the midwife a job. However, I hadn't been warned that painted toenails are not allowed in theatre, so the midwife removed the nail polish for me. I felt a bit awkward, her doing it for me, but my bump was so huge, it would've been tricky trying to do it myself.

We had been allocated a theatre time and were preparing for this, but then, there were a couple of emergencies, which understandably took precedence over us. It was therefore just a waiting game and yet more sitting around, becoming increasingly anxious, and of course, hungry. It also meant yet another change in midwife, as the second one was also called away to one of the emergencies.

Another Angel

I was then reminded that what we resist persists, because for weeks, I'd been going on and on about the fact that I absolutely didn't want the one and only male midwife on the ward assigned to me. In my small-minded way of understanding how things were at the time, I had concluded that a male midwife would have zero empathy, or indeed awareness, of my needs as a woman.

It was inevitable, therefore, that I was allocated the male midwife, only to discover how very wrong I was! And needless to say, I quickly learned that despite my initial resistance, he was everything I needed that morning, a true gift from the angels. He cared, he listened, and he laughed, helping to keep the energy light. The funny thing was the fact that he wasn't meant to be working that morning, but had been called in at the last minute to help out on the ward.

The Goddess of the Moon was dancing and for the first time during that pregnancy, I smiled at the manner in which events were unfolding. I'm pleased the Universe gave me the opportunity to recognise this, and to realise how judgmental I had been.

It wasn't long after he was assigned to me that, all of a sudden, they were ready for me in theatre. I had changed into a gown by then and removed my jewellery. I rushed off for yet another pee, with my kidneys now definitely in fight or flight mode, before settling myself on the bed again. A porter arrived to wheel me down to theatre, which seemed a bit ridiculous, as I could have quite easily walked.

I was upset to leave E in the ward, and I recall looking back at him as I was wheeled out of the ward and silently praying that he would join me soon. Unfortunately, birthing partners have to wait until you are prepped in theatre before they are allowed to join you. I didn't like the fact that we were separated at this scary time, and I felt sorry for him, left on the ward on his own. I was grateful for my male midwife, who did his best to keep me humoured during the short journey.

Arriving into the theatre waiting area was terrifying. While I've had surgery previously, I don't recall being in the theatre environment, so it was all new to me, and it felt like entering another world that I knew nothing about. I didn't recognise anyone, which is unusual here in Guernsey, and it felt really busy with the theatre staff rushing around.

A theatre nurse was assigned to me and she checked my nametag and asked me to confirm my name. I was trying to keep it all together, trying to smile, and trying to take it all in my stride, but it was challenging; my mind was in overdrive, concerned about the uncertainty of what lay ahead. My male midwife kept checking I was OK, and the theatre nurse asked me questions about yoga to try and keep me calm.

I found it difficult to concentrate though, as I had a myriad of ridiculous concerns going around in my head. Should I still be wearing my pants? No, and the kind nurse helped me to subtly remove these. Would my midwife definitely retrieve my placenta for me? Yes; he was primed with a plastic tub, I didn't need to worry. Would E be joining me soon? Yes, as soon we were settled in theatre.

I was handed a plastic hat to wear and we joked about this because we were all wearing them, and it was not the most attractive look. To reduce stomach acids ahead of all the medication I would soon be taking, I was given an antacid to drink. I wasn't happy about having to take anything that would impact on the balanced state of my gut, but I was aware that stomach acids can, in very rare cases, leak into a woman's lungs during a caesarean section, and it was necessary.

Soon, it was time to go into the theatre. It certainly wasn't the environment I would have chosen for the arrival of my baby into this world. It was bright, clinical and noisy, with the sound of equipment buzzing and the theatre staff busily preparing for the procedure. I was shifted from the ward bed on to the theatre bed, which made me feel awkward, as I didn't like to think that I wasn't capable of moving myself. I've never been so nervous and fearful.

My memory is a little hazy of the exact course of events, but I believe an intravenous line (IV) was placed into a vein on my right hand. This was used to deliver medications and fluids etc. during the surgery. It was also there if needed for a blood transfusion, and I was reminded that blood was available for me in the theatre, if it was required.

An oxygen-monitoring device was placed on my finger and a blood pressure cuff on my upper arm. I can't recall now whether wires connected to heart-monitoring equipment were attached to my chest, I just remember there being an awful lot of wires and equipment generally.

As soon as I was settled, I was then helped onto my left side so that the anaesthetist could apply the spinal anaesthesia. I was wearing a gown that opened at the back, so I felt exposed and vulnerable in front of a whole room of strangers. It was then that I became absolutely consumed by fear, especially that the anaesthetist might not be able to administer the epidural and so I would have to have a general anaesthetic.

I was aware I needed to stay still to assist the anaesthetist, but I was shaking uncontrollably. It was horrible because I just couldn't seem to make it stop. A kind nurse held my hand and talked me through some deep breathing to calm me down. I thought it was ironic that I had to be reminded of this, especially being a yoga teacher, but regardless, I was grateful for the support.

The focus on the breath made all the difference and I dropped my awareness deep into it, using Ujjayi breath, as this calms me down almost instantly. It was a very present-moment experience that I can still recall to this day. I was desperate to stop the shaking, and was doing all I could with the breath to do so.

I don't remember feeling any pain as the anaesthetist injected into and around the nerves of my spinal column, near the middle to lower back; I was just focused on being as still as possible. I was aware that once administered, the anaesthesia would give a rapid and complete numbing sensation, relaxing all the muscles of my legs and abdomen and preparing me for surgery.

It was the strangest feeling, especially when I had to touch various parts of my body at the anaesthetist's request to check whether the spinal had worked. My friend had already warned me about this – she said that while she was touching her own body, it felt like she was touching chicken breasts.

She was right; it felt very odd. It also felt very odd that I couldn't move my legs, and I wasn't entirely comfortable about this, as it made me feel claustrophobic. Still, this meant that the spinal had worked, and with that, I felt an incredible sense of relief. My greatest fear had not yet been realised, and hopefully, E would soon be able to join me.

I was aware of activity around me. The specialist in his surgeon capacity was busying himself to the lower right of me and the anaesthetist was positioned to my right chest, monitoring the screens. Soon, a screen was placed over my chest so that I couldn't see what was happening in front of me. My focus, however, was back towards the door behind me, and I kept crooking my neck around to look out for E, who was supposed to be joining me.

A nurse mentioned that they needed to move my legs to enable them to insert a flexible tube, a Foley catheter, into my bladder to drain urine and keep my bladder as empty as possible during the surgery. This was also a strange feeling, as I knew my legs were being moved but I couldn't actually feel them. Fortunately, I was too distracted by the door behind me to realise that this meant that my vagina was once again on display.

Finally, the door opened and there was E, dressed in his blue theatre attire, with the regulation plastic hat on his head. I could have wept with joy; it was an incredible relief that he was now able to join me. He was a little bit emotional at seeing me lying on the bed, attached to all the wires and machines, and the theatre staff primed for the birth, and quickly held my hand to comfort us both.

My relief was short lived, however, as I started to feel really sick. It probably didn't last long, as the anaesthetist reacted quickly, but it was long enough to send me into a minor panic. I felt helpless, as I was lying on my back, unable to move, and concerned that I was going to vomit. I quickly figured that I could turn my head to the side, if necessary, so I wouldn't choke, but nonetheless, it was a very scary feeling.

The anaesthetist explained that my blood pressure had dropped and she did what she could to balance the level again, and with that, the sickness eased. I wasn't very aware of what else was going on at that stage and I was trying to focus on my breath to steady myself, while gripping E's hand.

E was standing to my left side and watching the procedure over the screen in front of me. He later told me that it was incredibly graphic, but fascinating too, as he saw the different layers of muscle and fat as the surgeon operated. It wasn't long before I was told to expect some sensation of tugging and I could certainly feel this, but it wasn't painful.

Shortly after the tugging, I heard mention of the need for forceps and went into another minor panic because it hadn't crossed my mind that forceps would be needed during a caesarean birth. I expressed my concern to E, but he assured me that they were needed and were being used in a gentle manner. I shall never know if this was the case, and fortunately, I didn't have a lot of time to reflect on the use of them because moments later, the baby was born.

MEETING MY SON

We didn't know the sex ahead of the birth and we'd asked the specialist that E be the one to determine this. I remember E peering further forward over the screen as the baby was lifted out of me. I was impatient to know the sex and was asking him, "Is it a boy?" as this is what I had suspected throughout the pregnancy, and him nodding, before verbally confirming, with tears in his eyes, that our baby was a boy.

The name had chosen itself months beforehand. It had jumped out at me in the baby-naming book. E had agreed that he liked the name, and it just stuck. It wasn't a name I would ever have imagined myself choosing, but it fitted very well. Here he was, at 11.34a.m., on Tuesday 12th November 2013, thrust up in front of us above the screen for a very quick peak, our new-born son, Elijah Iain McInnes.

One of the meanings of the name "Elijah" is "miracle", which seemed appropriate to us as he was certainly our miracle, beating the odds by being conceived on our first attempt at IVF and staying safely in utero to 38.5 weeks, despite the placenta previa. The other meaning is strength and power, and that seemed appropriate too. He certainly felt strong and powerful, not least to beat the odds, but also with all the kicking he'd done in the womb.

We gave him his middle name, "Iain", after E's dad, who had passed away a few years before he and I met. We wanted to include him in Elijah's life in some way and hoped that by giving him his name, it would connect him somehow.

I have to be honest, I can't remember which came first, my first glimpse of my son lifted up above the screen or hearing his cry. I was told that babies don't need to cry upon birth, that actually, if their birth is peaceful, they need make no noise at all. However, I had also read that a good cry lets a baby test out his/her lungs for the first time.

Before a baby is born, it takes in oxygen through the placenta via the umbilical cord, but the moment the baby leaves the womb, it's on its own, so to speak. Natural instinct then kicks in and the baby does the only thing it can; it gives a good scream, the lungs fill up with air and, for the very first time, expand to their full capacity.

In addition, the baby's first cry helps them to get rid of any amniotic residue in the lungs, mouth and nasal passages. This can also be suctioned out by the nursing team, if required. That first cry indicates that the baby is breathing well on its own. Our little boy certainly seemed to have healthy lungs, and I welcomed that first cry.

I'm not sure of the exact sequence of events with the cord cutting either. Prior to the birth, I had read extensively about the benefit of delayed cord cutting, which include a normal, healthy blood volume for the transition to life outside the womb, and a full count of red blood cells, stem cells and immune cells. For the mother, delayed clamping is said to keep the mother-baby unit intact and can prevent complications with delivering the placenta.

However, as I had placenta previa I had been told that there was no time for delayed cord clamping, and with that, the loss of all the researched benefits. I knew this before going into surgery, so I had already had time to process this, but it still seemed desperately unfair that my little boy wasn't going to gain these additional benefits, having been plucked from my womb before he was ready.

Still, at least E was able to cut the cord. He had been resistant to this initially but now the opportunity presented itself, he was more than happy to get involved. It's often seen as a rite of fatherhood, or the first stage of forming a relationship between father and baby, and a Portuguese study found that the process aids emotional bonding between father and baby too. Whether it helped or not, I'll never know, but I was pleased E was involved in the process.

After the cord was cut and Elijah had his initial checks, our little miracle was soon brought to me as I lay on the bed while the specialist removed my placenta and stitched me up again. Fortunately, my placenta was retained by my midwife, as the wild yogini within me wanted to plant it in the garden to nourish a tree for Elijah – and so, the cycle would continue, with the tree providing oxygen and nourishing us all that way too.

I'll never forget seeing Elijah properly as he was placed skin to skin on my left side under my gown. He was wearing a pink and blue knitted hat, and looking so unfamiliar to me. I remember thinking, this is my son, but I don't recognise him, I don't know him and yet he's come from me.

I lost all sense of time after this. My blood pressure dropped again and I have no recollection of being moved from the theatre to the post-operative recovery area. E tells me that we were there for a good hour or so as I was stabilised, but to me, it felt like minutes.

All I remember is staring at Elijah and having the itchiest nose I had ever experienced. I just couldn't stop scratching it because the itch just wouldn't go away. The nurse administered an anti-histamine, which finally relieved it, but by then, the damage had been done; I'd scratched my nose red raw and it was scabby for days after.

Once I was stabilised and back in the land of the living, I was wheeled up to the ward, Elijah swaddled and asleep beside me, and E beside us. We had left the ward separately, E and I, and here we were, returning as a family of three. It was surreal but extremely exciting. I was now a mother with a healthy baby boy; it was a dream come true!

PART 4

Motherhood Begins

Chapter 19

Introduction to Motherhood

I was euphoric. I had a baby! I wanted to shout it from the rooftops, tell the whole world, invite them all in to have a peak, "Look, I have a baby, a little boy, my dream came true." I couldn't have been happier; I was flying high, that little bundle of joy swaddled in his cot beside my bed was all mine. He'd arrived.

I was joyous too because I'd survived theatre and E had gotten to see his son being born.

However, it was not how I had imagined birth. And this was certainly not how I imagined my introduction to motherhood. There was no champagne or lazy hours spent in our bed at home, admiring our new baby all on our own. There were no candles burning or soft music playing. There was none of the stuff I had hoped for when I had intended a homebirth.

Instead, here I was in hospital, wearing a blood-spattered hospital gown with a catheter attached to my bladder and a drip attached to my arm. My body was full of drugs from the surgery, including the obligatory antibiotics, which were killing all the good bacteria in my gut. And I was itchy, very itchy, as my body started to awaken from the anaesthetic. All I wanted to do was scratch.

I was also laying on what can only be described as a huge sanitary towel, with a smaller sanitary towel soaking up the blood trickling from my vagina. No one had told me that I would be bleeding from my vagina following the birth. Just like no one had told me that I would need a catheter and a drip and be unable to move from my bed. I didn't know any of this.

That first night, I couldn't sleep, because I was high on life and cups of tea, and because the hospital environment is not really conducive to resting, with all the midwife checks and the babies crying. I was slightly on edge too because I hadn't quite mastered breastfeeding by then and I wasn't quite sure what I would do if Elijah cried.

I was suddenly aware I was ill prepared for the reality of life with a new-born, and with this tiny person beside me, my "we'll just wing the baby bit" attitude seemed ever so slightly naïve. What was I thinking?!

Breastfeeding wasn't my only concern. Nor was knowing what to do when Elijah cried. It was more so the fact that I had such limited range of movement in my bed that I wasn't going to be able to do very much, regardless of the nature of his needs. And indeed, I couldn't do much, so that when he did cry because his nappy needed changing, the midwife had to tend to him, which I found desperately upsetting. I couldn't care for my own baby!

LEAVING THE HOSPITAL AND RECOVERY

The next day, the reality of recovery became glaringly obvious to me. It hurt to move. No one tells you this, do they? Just like no one told me that I was going to bleed for six weeks, or that my breasts, and indeed nipples, would get really sore, or that I would have to wear those hideous compression stockings for a good 10 days at home, or that I would struggle to walk upstairs without feeling like I may collapse due to the blood loss I'd experienced during the birth, and the lack of iron in my body.

I was keen to have the catheter removed first thing and, with the help of painkillers, I winced my way to the toilet, as I was determined to get on with life as normal. Taking a shower later that morning felt amazing, albeit exhausting, and I remember staring aghast in the mirror at my post-pregnancy body, not recognising it.

Admittedly, my bump was deflating quickly, but it was still very evident and felt strange knowing that the baby was no longer in there. I was very pale too and had a scabby nose from all the scratching, and now, I had this new scar below my bikini line, which was sore and bruised. I felt all saggy. I stood under the water, holding onto the wall, head down, and just let the water wash over me, cleansing me.

I had been told to invest in some high-waist leggings and big pants to wear post-surgery, and I was grateful to my friend for the tip. Both of these made a huge difference in ensuring minimal pressure on my wound. The leggings also helped to hide those horrible stockings (although I sneaked these off whenever I could, as I was mobile and practicing yoga (of sorts) within a few days).

I was delighted to be told I could go home after two sleepless nights in the hospital. I was looking forward to my own bed and enjoying some peace and quiet after the noise on the ward, with babies crying and people coming and going. I was also keen to eat some healthy food again and get on my mat, even if I just lay there.

Unfortunately, I had lost so much blood during the birth that I was on the borderline for a blood transfusion, which I refused. I just didn't like the idea of taking on someone else's blood and energy. However, this did mean that I was not allowed to be left on my own when I returned home and I was very weak. I questioned my decision in the weeks that followed. I shall never forget leaving the hospital, walking to the car park and being so out of breath and feeling so weak that I had to support myself on the car. I shall also never forget arriving home and struggling up the stairs and having to sit down at the top to recover.

This was my main memory of leaving hospital and returning home. That and putting Elijah into his car seat at the hospital in his huge all-in-one outfit and suddenly realising that he was really quite tiny! It felt strange being back at home with a baby, and there was this overwhelming sense of responsibility, and also a slight anxiety about what to do if he cried and I couldn't somehow comfort him. We were still getting to know one another and this was my first real exposure to a new-born baby.

My Mum and E rushed around, trying to get the cottage warm, as we hadn't been given much notice before I was discharged. I unpacked my bag and was concerned about how uncomfortable it was to move around and how light-headed I felt. I really didn't feel well and I wasn't quite sure how I was going to care for a baby, when I needed to be cared for myself. As I quickly learned, you don't have much choice as a new mother, you just have to get on with it, however awful you feel.

What also felt strange, aside from having our own baby in the cottage, was not knowing what to do with myself. New-born babies sleep a lot, and here I was, on a weekday afternoon, sitting on the sofa, holding a sleeping baby, and not having anything in particular to do, no deadline to meet. I rarely sit on the sofa in the afternoon, as I'm usually rushing around working, and it felt a little surreal sitting still, doing nothing, and having cups of tea made for me.

It didn't take long for me to reach for my Blackberry, however, and make a start on catching up on all the work emails I had missed while I'd been in hospital. I also had a blog post to write and congratulatory emails to respond to from friends, so I soon made myself busy, because that's normal for me, although I hadn't factored in all the visitors and how time-consuming (and tiring) their visits could be.

Admittedly, those first few days in the hospital, and then back at home, I was still euphoric. My dream had come true, and I was blown away with the love I felt for this little being, who was a part of E and I. It was nothing short of a miracle, and I was incredibly grateful. I wanted to show Elijah to the world, and I made sure to share photos on Facebook and sent out a newsletter to those on my mailing list, sharing our good news. We were inundated with deliveries of flowers, cards and presents, and received lots of emails and messages of congratulations.

It was mind-blowing, like entering a whole new world – people seemed genuinely happy that we'd had a baby. I found all the attention both uplifting and incredibly overwhelming. I'll never forget the delivery of a huge, cuddly teddy bear from my work. It was so huge that it took up half of the dining room table – both Mum and I were in hysterics about it. I love that teddy, as it represents all the love that was directed to us at the time and the craziness of it all.

However, after a few days, I was feeling the exhaustion, and I was struggling with all the visitors, family and friends, and even neighbours, who wanted to see Elijah for themselves.

In many respects, the visiting was the hardest bit, because my home is my sanctuary, and I can be really rather antisocial at times! It was lovely of course that everyone wanted to meet Elijah and have a cuddle with him, but I was just feeling so utterly drained from the blood loss that it was often a real effort to maintain my positive humour and have the energy for conversation.

I came to realise the reason that in some spiritual circles, couples with new babies often take at least a week – one tradition I've read about taking 40 days – to just be by themselves without any visitors. It is believed that this helps with the bonding process, and setting the energetics of the new family without outside energetics (of other people) disrupting this. Certainly, my brother and his fiancé, who birthed their daughter at home, took time alone those first few days following the birth to just be as a family.

But we were the complete opposite to this. In part, it was my own making, in that I wasn't very good at saying "no". Although actually, there were times when people just showed up at the front door, so there was very little one could do but welcome them in. If I had been feeling better, and my usual bouncy self, then perhaps it wouldn't have been such a problem.

I took on board a wise suggestion from a friend and kept a note of the gifts we received from each person – this became an invaluable list a few weeks later when it came to sending out thank you cards and remembering who had sent what. As I quickly came to recognise, sleep deprivation and having a new-born in your life does nothing to support the memory function - I found my memory was slowly disappearing, and I couldn't blame the wine!

Not that I rushed back to drinking wine. I like a glass of wine, but I was feeling so incredibly rubbish that I didn't even feel I could toast the birth with a glass of champagne - that's saying something! Instead, I drank an awful lot of black tea. Sleep deprivation and exhaustion seem to go hand in hand with black tea, which is silly really, as it simply exacerbates the situation, in terms of giving you false energy, and all the caffeine making it difficult to sleep! Plus, too much tea can rob the body of nutrients, but that's all I wanted to drink at the time. That and copious amounts of water to flush all the toxins from the medication out of my system.

I was constipated for three whole days following the birth, which just added to my general level of discomfort. I loathe being constipated and was frustrated that the antibiotics had adversely affected the balance of microbes in my gut; I usually resist them for this very reason. I took probiotics and ate yoghurt to increase the levels of good bacteria and consumed seeds, fruit and brown rice, as well as drinking a whole heap of water in a quest to empty my bowels.

However, there was a psychological aspect to this too; the scar was so painful that subconsciously, I was very fearful of creating yet more pain through the pushing action of defecating. The mere hint of a sneeze had me panicking because sneezing hurt. A lot. As did coughing or any sudden movement. It sucked. I was given medication to soften the stools, but stopped these, along with all medication, that first day I returned home from the hospital, as I just wanted to give my liver a break and heal my body holistically.

I took some milk thistle to support my liver, and also to increase my milk supply. I took arnica remedy to help with my internal healing, and I used a combination of arnica cream, tea tree oil and lavender oil on my scar to heal this too. I found that rubbing arnica onto my skin where the bump had been helped with this contracting, and I channelled Reiki onto myself at any given opportunity.

It was a relief when my digestive system started working properly again. There's such a connection between the gut and the mind, that when you've a whole heap of toxins stuck inside you, it starts to change the way you feel, and I didn't need anything else throwing me off balance, as I was having a hard enough time as it was. I'd completely lost my grounding; it was like the rug had been pulled from under my feet.

CRASH

Due to the fact I'd lost so much blood, I wasn't allowed to be left on my own in case I collapsed or fainted. This in itself was a challenge, as I love being on my own, it's what I do best, pottering until my heart's content, and enjoying solitude and silence. So it was tough always having to have someone in the house with me, and of course, not being able to drive, so that I felt my wings were truly clipped – I struggled with this as much as I struggled with every other aspect of the post-natal period.

It took 5 days before I crashed. My mum had expected it earlier and was concerned I was going a little too hyper. I'd been warned that the tears may arrive with the milk on day three, and there was a part of me that naively thought maybe I'd gotten away with it. But alas, not. On the fifth day, I couldn't stop crying and I felt incredibly sensitive, insecure and low. It threw me; what did I have to feel low about? I had a baby, I should have been continuously happy forever more.

However, it's all part of the process, as the hormones do their thing, and the exhaustion begins to kick in. It did make me think though that we often believe certain events or changes to our life will bring us continuous happiness, but there's often always a challenge. This challenge was partly hormonal and partly due the fact that my world as I knew it had been well and truly turned upside down. I didn't have a clue how to find my grounding again. The last few years, the focus had primarily been about having a baby, and now

I had the baby, I felt a little directionless and a little thrown off balance, because the reality of having a baby was very different to what I had imagined.

I know I'm not alone. A huge shift occurs when women become mothers for the first time, which can often lead to a period of shock. Not only do they tend to lose blood, and with that, iron and their magnetic, and indeed energetic, connection to the Earth itself, but their whole identity and sense of self changes. Life is no longer all about them – as it tends to be during pregnancy, at least the first pregnancy – and now, there's this other little being demanding their attention, and their own needs become secondary to that.

There's this fabulous quote from Uma Dinsmore-Tuli in her book, *Yoni Shakti*, that sums it up perfectly.

"*For a postnatal woman, the experience of transformation is direct, bloody and embodied. Whatever kind of birth a woman experiences, the transition from being pregnant to being a mother is an immense and rapid transformation at every dimension of being, from the visceral to the spiritual. At a physical level, the body changes overnight from a living embodiment of ripe fullness into an empty and often damaged and exhausted shell. Even after the most positive birth experience, the postnatal body can be left bleeding, leaking and broken. The shift in hormone levels is like falling off a cliff, or going cold turkey from class-A drugs. From the astonishing experience of peak levels of pregnancy and birth hormones (the feel-good progesterone, oestrogen and endorphins that facilitate the super-human endeavours of late pregnancy and labour, and the massive adrenalin kick that actually births the baby), a postnatal woman encounters a dramatic hormonal drop, accompanied by a chaotic vortex of shifting patterns of endocrine activity.*"

Fortunately, I was fully supported during this challenging time. My mum virtually moved in to make sure I wasn't on my own during the day. This meant that E could continue his life as usual, and while I was initially aggrieved that he didn't take any time off when I initially came home from hospital, I came to realise that this was his way of coping with the significant shift in our lives. He works for himself and he just didn't see the point in sitting around at home with me, Elijah and my mum, when he could be earning money for us.

This did present issues for us later, however, as he lacked an understanding of what having a baby at home entailed. By the time he returned home from work, all the chores were done, the washing was up to date and dinner was in the oven. This was all my mum's doing, may I add; she did everything for me, well, for us really, those first few weeks, because I just didn't have the energy.

I was so pleased to have the extra help. I sweated so badly at night those first few weeks that the sheets would get wet, which I believe was my body's way of trying to release the after-effects of the drugs from my system (that, and the shock on my body of night-time waking to breastfeed), so these needed to be washed daily. Plus, there was all the extra baby washing – I had no idea that a baby could create so much washing!

I also hadn't realised that breastfeeding was a full-time occupation, and while the opportunity to sit down was appreciated from an energetic perspective, I wasn't used to it, and I often felt that I should be doing something instead. I watched a lot of television during this time, which was also strange to me, and while it was a novelty initially, I soon tired of it. I also used the opportunity to respond to work emails because I couldn't switch off from this and still felt the pressure to work.

I also quickly realised that breastfeeding demanded a certain style of dressing, especially in winter time, a vest that could be pulled down from the top and a top that could be rolled up from below to reveal the nipple, or a button-down top. It's knowing stuff like this that certainly makes a difference in navigating through this confusing time. It did mean a huge percentage of my wardrobe, including all my dresses, would remain unused for some time.

(NOT) LISTENING TO MY BODY

I was desperate to get back on my yoga mat, and while I certainly wasn't able to do that in hospital (what had I been thinking?!), I made sure to get on it as soon as I could once I was back at home. Initially, I just lay on it and breathed, before incorporating some gentle movement in an effort to relieve the congestion in my digestive system and try to energise my system again.

It wasn't long, though, before I was desperate to actively move my body and practice as I had done previously, in a yang and active manner. It didn't matter to me that I'd just had major abdominal surgery or that I was exhausted from this and from the sleep deprivation, I just wanted some anchoring in my life again, and this way of practicing came naturally to me. In my naivety, I felt it would benefit me physically and mentally, bring me back to Earth a little.

In hindsight, it was silly of me, yet, it was also an essential part of my yoga journey and learnings. I eventually came to realise that, if anything, this approach to practice, especially in the post-natal period, was without doubt creating further energetic imbalance within me and stressing my body and mind, yet I couldn't see it at the time. I was desperately clinging onto anything that felt normal, even if it wasn't actually enhancing my wellbeing.

It's a lesson we learn; the one about letting go and surrendering. But there I was, with babe in arms, and still, I wasn't dancing with the Goddess of the Moon and allowing her energy to flow through me. I was still taking a masculine approach to yoga and to life, despite absolutely needing the softness and compassion of the feminine at that time, and it took me a few more years to realise this.

I just found those early weeks so incredibly challenging. I was so "gung-ho" about the transition to motherhood and what this would entail. My life, for 38 years, had been about me, doing what I wanted when I wanted, and now, it felt like that freedom had been taken away.

So, a little like with my yoga practice, I compounded my exhaustion by doing the things I used to do previously to maintain some sanity when it felt like everything else around me was totally out of control. This meant that, five weeks post-caesarean section, I went running. I felt like I needed to get out of the house, get into nature, clear my head, and feel alive again. On some level, I was also trying to run my life forwards.

It was insane, now I think back. There I was, with milk-filled breasts and a tugging scar, running through the lanes near our cottage in the centre of the island, simply because I needed some fresh air, freedom and space to process all that had happened. I would never encourage any new mother to do this. During the immediate post-natal period, let alone post-surgery, the body needs rest, not to be pushed like this, and a gentle walk would have been more appropriate.

Still, I was listening to my body in other ways. I had been trying to increase my iron levels through my vegetarian diet by eating vast quantities of dried apricots, spinach and dark chocolate, but I didn't feel like they were having any significant impact. If anything, all the sugar was simply encouraging the growth of candida and creating a greater imbalance in my gut flora, which was already struggling due to the antibiotics and my lowered immune function.

So I finally relented and, much to my family's relief, I agreed to eat red meat, which I hadn't eaten for many, many years. My mum made me a shepherd's pie, as she felt that this would make it easier to eat. Well, I certainly didn't have any problem eating it. It was an animalistic experience, as I was salivating at the sight and smell of it, and I simply couldn't get enough of it and ate it with such vigour that E was astounded, as he'd never seen me eat meat previously.

It was an empowering experience because for once, I was truly listening to and honouring the needs of my body, in a way that I hadn't done previously. It wasn't easy though, and I had to dig deep to make peace with this on a soul level – I feel strongly about animal welfare and killing animals for our pleasure, so it helped to see it as a short-term medicine. The meat-medicine worked, and I'm very grateful to the animals who helped me to heal. It took a few months, but my iron levels increased, and I reached a point where I no longer needed to eat meat and I returned to my vegetarian diet.

Six weeks from the birth

Six weeks post-surgery, I had a check-up with the specialist who had carried out the caesarean section, and by then, my scar had healed. I could still feel it when running, but I wasn't aware of it other than that. The vaginal bleeding had also stopped and I was finally able to drive again. I was also well enough now to be left on my own again, and I relished this. I was still extremely exhausted though; the sleep deprivation was beginning to take its toll and little did I realise at that time that this would go on for many years!

I loved Elijah, of course, but I remember at his six-week check with the doctor, saying to the doctor that I wasn't sure how anyone could want more than one, as one was such hard work.

I was very well aware that we still had one blastocyst and two frozen embryos stored at Wessex, and I felt this urgency to do something with them. The doctor told me to let that go and just concentrate on Elijah, and she was right.

I was still feeling pretty overwhelmed, however, and there were lots of tears and moments of frustration. It just took so long to do anything, to get Elijah changed and ready to leave the house, and then inevitably, we'd need to have another nappy change, and that would add on another 10 minutes, so we were always running late. I was beginning to anger quickly too, due to a combination of the sleep deprivation and the fatigue, and I blamed the caesarean section for all of this. I was still hung up on the fact that this wasn't how it was meant to be!

I was also angry because my expectations were not being met. Without meaning to, I had an expectation of birth, of motherhood, of having a baby, of what E should or shouldn't do to help, and my expectations were not being met. Life was certainly challenging those next few months, and I looked forward to my evening glass of wine, which would help me to wind down into the evening, sitting as I was on the sofa by then, babe in arms.

It actually took me a few years to heal from this birth experience and the shock of the transition to motherhood. I couldn't understand the reason any woman would elect to have a caesarean section, or have another baby, and I had increased compassion and respect for all mothers. My healing and spiritual journey would help me to finally come to terms with this experience, because as I would later discover, that which you resist persists... and the Goddess of the Moon was still waiting for me to dance with her.

Chapter 20

Sleep Deprivation and Adjusting to Motherhood

Sleep deprivation brings you to your knees. It's no surprise it's used as a form of torture. I certainly felt like I was being persecuted at times, and it affected my perception of reality. This wasn't what I'd signed up for. Motherhood was all-consuming and I longed for something to shift, for Elijah to sleep, for E and I to have some fun, and for life to become brighter again. There is absolutely nothing that can prepare you for the reality of the sleep deprivation that accompanies night-time feeding – and I was most certainly no exception.

Towards the end of my pregnancy, I lost count of the number of people who told me to get the sleep while I could. It used to really annoy me because it was nigh on impossible to get any decent sleep, due to the discomfort of sleeping with a huge bump and the constant need to pee. I considered it nature's way of preparing me for what lay ahead, but it didn't really. It just meant I was tired before I'd even had the baby.

I quickly gave up with the "trying to settle Elijah thing". I had his Moses basket right beside the bed but he absolutely loathed going in this initially, and I found that the only way to settle him was if he slept on my chest with me sleeping virtually upright, propped up on pillows. I've since discovered that this is common in those first few weeks, and perhaps not surprising, given that the baby has been nestled inside you all those months and wants to stay close to you.

Breaking the "rules"

I was a little nervous about this at first, given the fact it had been drilled into me in hospital that you must not have the baby sleep with you in your bed (I got told off in hospital for doing this one night), but I absolutely needed sleep and this was the only way I could manage it. It was never enough sleep though, and as E returned to work immediately after I returned home from hospital, and as my breasts were frequently required for feeding, I didn't get to lie in either.

After six weeks of Elijah lying on my chest, I was desperate to lie on my side to sleep. By then, my shoulders, neck and upper back were aching from all the breastfeeding, carrying of car seats, and my awful posture when it came to the night-time feeding. I was often so tired that it was all I could do not to fall asleep as I was leaning over, breastfeeding him. I was severely anaemic and had such little energy. All I longed for was a good night's sleep.

I managed to transfer Elijah into the Moses basket, albeit that the Moses basket was placed in the centre of the bed between E and I. Fortunately, we had invested in a super king-sized bed in preparation for his arrival, and already, this was proving beneficial, as it meant we still had lots of space. It was lovely to sleep as I chose, and he was still close by, and amazingly, it didn't take much longer to settle him than it had done when he slept on my chest.

Putting him on his front helped him to settle. We had little choice, as he wouldn't sleep on his back, and I don't blame him, it's not a position I favour either, but we felt hugely guilty placing him to sleep on his tummy, as this, once again, went against all the guidelines that you're given in respect of safe baby sleeping. Still, it felt intuitively OK to take that perceived risk, and my mum and her friends were very much of the opinion that they'd slept their babies like that, so what was the big deal. I tended to agree.

I had been keen to mother Elijah intuitively, but when it came down to it, as a first-time mum, I was fearful of unintentionally doing something to harm him and often sought validation that what I was doing was OK. I was a member of various baby-related Facebook groups back in those days and would get regular updates from Baby Centre about what my baby should be doing and when.

I quickly became aware that there is a myriad of opinions on how best to raise a baby. Often, mothers would present their opinion and validate it by including a link to a relevant research paper. Now, I certainly have no wish to discredit researchers and the often valuable work they do, but research findings can be decidedly biased, depending on who's funding it, the nature of the research subjects used, and the manner in which the research is interpreted.

The research would often ignore the fact that every baby is different, every mother is different, and mothers should be given an opportunity to go with the flow. It is my experience that far too often in life, we are not given the opportunity, or encouraged to truly check in with our intuition and our gut feelings, and trust in these, and have the strength to act upon them.

Many women don't even know how to access their innate voice, because they've spent the best part of their life making decisions based on other people's opinions, be that their parents, partners, siblings, friends or society. This lack of connection with natural insight, and our inability to make decisions based on it, merely serves to make motherhood an even trickier, disorientating and confusing time than it is already.

People would so readily give their opinion, and this took some getting used to. Even complete strangers would comment on whether Elijah looked hot, or enquire into his sleeping and feeding patterns and offer unrequested advice. Perhaps it's no surprise then that the majority end up doing things by the book – whatever the book may say at that particular time – even if it doesn't resonate with that mother or isn't right for her baby or her immediate family.

I fell into this trap with Elijah. It was ridiculous really, because up until that point, at least since I'd been practicing yoga and Reiki, I had been living my life intuitively. However, having a baby was new to me and I was so extremely exhausted and ungrounded that even if I did experience some clarity, I always felt that everyone else knew better than I did, and initially, I felt a pressure to conform to what was expected of me as a responsible mother (whatever that meant).

I had been told that babies often start sleeping better at six weeks, so I was hanging out for this. But the six-week anniversary came and went and there was no much-needed positive change. He was still waking every two hours. The fact I was still terribly anaemic didn't help, nor that I was often having to check the Blackberry and keep abreast of developments at work. I was running on empty and desperate for sleep.

The 12-week anniversary was soon upon us, and with that, my return to work. Still, the sleep didn't improve, and if anything, it got worse. It was as if he needed the night-time intimacy to make up for the fact I was now parted from him for up to five hours a day. It didn't help that this coincided with his teething, and he would sometimes wake every hour, or even more than this at times.

Exhaustion

I felt permanently jetlagged and existed on black tea and dark chocolate in quantities I had never before consumed, or indeed since. The job was demanding, as I was on a three-month catch up with a never-ending inbox, and there was lots going on that was both time-consuming to deal with and urgent. Additionally, I now had to factor in time away from my desk to express milk, and I had to be really disciplined in taking the time to do this.

It also didn't help that I now had baby brain and acute sleep deprivation, which created an inability to retain information for longer than five minutes. I was OK if I could stay in my zone, but the moment anyone asked me a question, I would lose the thread of what I had just been doing and sit there, staring at my screen, completely baffled and incapable of thinking clearly.

It was the most frustrating experience, so too the inability to remember words, so I was frequently asking my male colleague the most ridiculous questions. Fortunately, he had a young family himself so he was well aware of what I was going through. But still, I had to check and re-check my work because I would make silly little mistakes, which was infuriating for a type A personality! I began to think that I was going mad.

And then, I did go mad.

Well, not mad in the sense that I lost my mind entirely, just mad in the sense that, as the weeks went on and the night feeding and waking continued at one to two-hourly intervals, I found myself on an edge. The cumulative effects of the sleepless nights began to take their toll. I was incredibly angry about the birth, the resulting anaemia, and the manner in which this had affected my health. It had left me with recurring thrush infections and a compromised immune system.

I had completely lost my grounding, and with this, I had also lost my footing. I was surviving each day, obsessed with my tiredness and my inability to think clearly, I felt directionless and unsupported, and I was angry at the Universe. The dark night of the soul was upon me. This was not how I imagined motherhood to be; it was exhausting and relentless, and was seriously affecting my relationship with E, which had been good up until this point.

My life became one of constant rushing. I'd get myself and Elijah ready for the day, go to work, and try and get on top of things, and then I'd rush away from work to collect Elijah, and inevitably, I was always running late and aware that Elijah would be wanting breast milk. I'd feed him at my parents' house and then return home mid-afternoon to washing that needed hanging up, dinner that needed preparing, a house that needed tidying, and a baby who would cry unless I was holding him. Then, once a week, I would teach yoga in the evenings too.

My life felt terribly out of control and it was no surprise perhaps that my OCD need for cleanliness went into overdrive. It became imperative, back in those days, that the kitchen floor was spotless, and I wasted a good few cumulative hours of my life cleaning this for 10 minutes each day. My yoga practice became even more important to me, as it provided a lifeline, a sanctuary, a quiet space without anyone demanding anything of me.

Really, I should have just adopted a gentle practice with a lot of resting, but I challenged myself too much. It took me until Elijah was two years old to appreciate my profound tiredness and the need for a gentle and restorative practice, and the benefits that this would offer me physically, mentally, emotionally and spiritually. I've since discovered the joy of Uma Dinsmore-Tuli and her incredibly feminine and healing approach to the yoga during the post-natal period.

TAKING ITS TOLL ON E

It was the exhaustion that made everything so challenging. I just didn't have the same energy for life. I certainly didn't have any energy for E either. This was another shift. All the attention I previously gave to him, I gave to Elijah, and I had absolutely no interest in him touching me. Pre-baby, I'd been very tactile, but now, I felt like my body was for Elijah, and I couldn't cope with anyone else touching it. My libido was at an all-time low! It was a particularly challenging year, and there were times when I didn't think that we would make it.

E didn't seem to understand, and was constantly frustrated at my low mood and obsession with how much sleep I wasn't getting. The fact he didn't understand just compounded matters, and with that, the resentment set in, and I had no idea how to change things. Resentment is a horrible energy, all woody and edgy so that it splits things apart, and certainly, there were moments where it was doing that to us.

I now know that this is perfectly normal, in that many couples go through a significant period of adjustment during the first year of parenthood. The dynamics of the relationship change, the mother is often exhausted and trying hold it all together with the home, the baby and work, while the father's life appears to continue as usual, albeit, he now has to adjust to someone else demanding his partner's attention. It didn't help that we came to parenthood late, when we were both so used to doing what we wanted, when we wanted.

The father doesn't always appreciate the significant change that the mother's body has had to go through either, not least to accommodate the pregnancy, but post-natal too. There's often weight gain and you don't feel so good about yourself, and you might be breastfeeding and have full and leaky breasts. Factor in sore bits from the birth and all the hormonal shifts happening, and it is hardly surprising women just want to be left alone at this time.

I found the changes to my body one of the most difficult aspects of the initial post-natal period. That and the sleep deprivation. Not only was I giving mentally and emotionally, but now, I was giving physically as well, and I certainly didn't have any energy to give to E too. Because I was so sick, this just compounded matters, and occasionally, I just wanted someone else to manage everything so I could have some time off from all the responsibility!

I'd desperately wanted to have a baby and now, I was questioning whether I had been right to encourage E to have that baby with me. I'd had this terribly romantic idea of how things should be, breastfeeding and floating around with a baby attached to me, whereas the reality was completely different. I was super sensitive to everything and would cry easily. The tiredness was all-consuming and I didn't know how to change things.

GETTING DESPERATE

Fortunately, I had befriended a lovely mum with a little boy just a month older than Elijah, who helped to keen me sane. She, too, was going through the same experience, so we were able to moan and share together. We were also keen to find a solution that meant we got more sleep. We were both keen to parent gently (gentle parenting, it's called), so the "crying it out" approach was never an option for either of us.

The only time I read a baby-related book was in my quest for more sleep. I tried the *No Cry Sleep Solution*, by Elizabeth Pantley, which was all very well and good, but to be honest, I was just too tired to put any of it into practice! I just simply didn't have the energy to make a change; breastfeeding when Elijah awoke seemed the quickest and easiest way for us to get back to sleep, even if everyone told us that this was creating the sleeping issue.

I tried all sorts of other things. We went to baby yoga, and while we both enjoyed the classes, they didn't make him sleep any better. I took him for cranial-osteopathy and to see a healer too, and while both ladies told me he would sleep better after the sessions, he never did. I burned lavender oil in his room and wafted pine essential oil into his aura to ground him. I gave him Bach floral remedies and homeopathic remedies.

We bathed in Dead Sea salts to cleanse our auras and I put crystals under his pillow. We spent a lot of the day outside in nature, running around and getting lots of fresh air. I practiced Reiki on him, but while others are calmed and sleep amazingly well after receiving Reiki, typically, it seemed to make no difference to him at all (I've since come to recognise that his is because our energies are so similar). I used the soothing sounds of Tranquil Turtle too (one of those toys that is marketed as a way to help babies to sleep by playing soothing music and lightening the room blue), but this seemed to soothe me more than it did him.

Of course, there was always hope that the sleep would improve, and it was this hope that my friend and I lived off. It got to the point where we would laugh because someone was always telling us that when we reached certain milestones, things would change, for example, when they started on solids, when they started crawling etc. But those milestones came and went and made no difference to our sons' respective sleeping patterns; if anything, they got worse.

E and I did what was encouraged and moved Elijah into a cot when he outgrew the Moses basket. Intuitively, I had intended to co-sleep, but I was told that I would be making a rod for my own back, and that he would smell my milk and want to feed even more than he did already. In hindsight, it was silly, because I just spent half my night traipsing backwards and forwards across the bedroom to feed him and try to settle him in the cot that he didn't like to sleep in.

Sometimes, I was up and down every 45 minutes, which was incredibly tough. It was at times like this that I felt wholly resentful of E sleeping soundly beside me. There was little he could do, however, as Elijah was very attached to me and would want the comfort of my cuddle and my breast, but nonetheless, I was still annoyed E didn't appreciate the extent of my tiredness.

Mind you, it's difficult to truly explain how detrimental a lack of sleep can be to one's wellbeing, or indeed, how you manage to keep on going. But you do, because each night, you hope it will be better. I lived and breathed sleep deprivation and I made sure everyone knew about it. It became my thing. It was hard for it not to be though, as it impacted so hugely on my quality of life and my health.

Essentially, I needed help, but I didn't know how to ask for it, and I couldn't see how anyone could help because I wasn't prepared to stop breastfeeding. People told me I needed to move Elijah into his own room, as he'd sleep better farther away from us. We tried this and now I just spent half my night walking backwards and forward across the landing, instead of backwards and forwards across the bedroom. So we moved him back into our room, where he stayed until he was big enough to go straight into his own bed, when he was about 17 months or so.

We put him on a double mattress on the floor initially, and we were told that this was the reason he continued to keep waking – that it was too big for him and he'd be scared, waking up with all this space around him. So we replaced it with a proper single bed with a rail along the side of it to stop him falling out of bed, but this made no difference. I was still spending half my night in his room and now, it just meant there was less space for me in the bed beside him. So, I'd end up just carrying him into the bed with us, where he'd wrap his arms around my neck and hang on until the morning.

It felt like things would never change, and by the time Elijah was about 18 months, I was just about keeping a grip on things. I'd done an eight-week mindfulness course a few months earlier and that had made me very aware that my life was out of balance and that I was stressed and unhappy. It wasn't just the sleep deprivation that was challenging, my working life was far too busy, I was approaching my 40th birthday, and knew that we still had frozen embryos in Wessex.

Furthermore, as I have explained, I was under pressure from E and other family members to stop breastfeeding, and I knew that if we went through another round of IVF, that I would have to do this before the treatment began. However, I was adamant that I wanted to breastfeed until he was two so he could gain the immunity benefits. Not that I told anyone, but I had some concerns that I wasn't mentally or physically in the "right" place for IVF and was concerned I never would be.

GETTING HELP

I ended up seeing a counsellor because I just needed to talk to someone who didn't know me and who wouldn't judge me, so that I could try to make sense of how to make things better again. I'm not sure the counselling itself helped, but the fact I had acknowledged that I needed help set the wheels in motion and I slowly started to make the necessary changes to the way I was living to help me to heal.

I recognised that the more I went on about being tired, the more I was going to create "tired" in my life; it's the law of attraction. I also realised that I needed to take my need for sleep more seriously. I had to go to bed earlier and slow my life down to facilitate this. I had to stop juggling so many balls and trying to be superwoman. I had to accept my imperfections and that it was OK to rest and let things be (like the kitchen floor).

I also finally learned to accept that Elijah just didn't need much sleep. I acknowledged that there was nothing wrong with him and stopped looking for the magic sleep solution, because it didn't exist. One day, I knew that we would have the opposite issue – we wouldn't be able to get him out bed in the morning – so I resolved to accept what I couldn't change and appreciate the blessing of my energetic little boy instead. It was me who needed to change, not him.

Chapter 21

The Joy of Breastfeeding

During my pregnancy, there was a local campaign to encourage more women to breastfeed. I didn't need any encouragement, as I was desperate to breastfeed. But equally, I didn't want to be pressurised into a state of anxiety about whether I could actually breastfeed, and E and I were very much of the opinion that we would wait and see what happened.

In my ideal world, as I have mentioned before, I would have birthed vaginally and peacefully at home, and the baby would have immediately latched on to my breast and that would have been it, job done! Sadly, this was not the case, especially as I was not feeling very well immediately post-surgery, and it wasn't until I was back up on the ward that I was encouraged to try and get Elijah to latch on.

Easier said than done, however, and the first few attempts didn't go well at all. I was aware that the pressure was rising, but E and I had it in mind that when Elijah needed to feed, he would feed.

I distinctly remember a number of midwives trying to help Elijah latch onto me using all different sorts of techniques – I was completely thrown by the rugby-style approach (holding the baby from your waist to latch on, rather than across your front; it looked and felt desperately uncomfortable to me!), and I am in awe of women who adopt this.

In the end, it was my marvellous male midwife who helped Elijah latch on, which I found nothing short of incredible. This was karma really, because there I'd been, at the beginning of the day, loathing the idea of a male midwife, as I thought he would lack empathy and an awareness of how to help a pregnant, and then post-natal, lady, but he was exactly the help I needed.

It was amazing and yet equally strange that first time. The sensation was much stronger than I had imagined, and I had this sense of the enormity of the task at hand – I was my son's sole source of nourishment, I had to make this work.

In the days that followed, it was tough. My nipples became really sore and it hurt to feed Elijah. I'd find myself wincing and thinking that surely, this couldn't be right, but apparently it is perfectly normal to feel like this. It was also very new to me, and I was concerned about how I was holding him and whether he was feeding properly.

Under pressure

When I returned home, there was an enormous (external) pressure for him to put on weight. I'm not surprised so many women give up trying to breastfeed and go immediately to the bottle, because I was made to feel as if something was wrong with my milk, or that I wasn't breastfeeding him properly. The visiting midwife told me that if he didn't start putting on more weight, he was either going to have to return to hospital, or we would have to start supplementing with formula.

It was ridiculous. There you are, a new mum, trying to do your best, only to be told that your best isn't good enough, and perhaps you don't have enough milk to feed your own baby. Cue feeling disempowered all over again. So, then, in my infinite wisdom (not so wise as it happens), I tried to massage milk from my breast into my nipple, which resulted in me flooding Elijah and giving him excess wind.

It wasn't until a lovely, calming Irish midwife came around to the cottage and shared the magic words, "Nose to nipple, tum to mum", that we truly "got" the breastfeeding. Why had no one told me this earlier? Unbeknown to me at that time, I had been unintentionally squashing Elijah's nose into my breast so that the poor thing couldn't breathe, which didn't make for a particularly restful feeding time!

Plus, I'd been switching breasts too quickly in a mission to make sure he got plenty of milk, but had been giving him lots of foremilk, which is watery, rather than the fattier (and filling) hind milk. And of course, with the breast massage and the squashed nose, it was hardly surprising he ended up with lots of wind. I also hadn't worked out, at that stage, that what I ate made a difference too; for example, dairy made him very snuffly with mucus and soya made him particularly windy.

My mum would talk about him being blue above his mouth, and how this was an indication that he still had wind, but I just couldn't see this. My auntie took this to another level, because she could actually feel the wind while she was rubbing his back. I can feel energy and auras and chakras, but I couldn't feel the wind in Elijah's body and I felt that my auntie must certainly have a gift.

Others had this gift too, as they would visit and wind my baby for me in half the time it seemed to take me. It was certainly not a skill of mine, and I was quite happy for anyone else to take control of this. This was the bit that I found most exhausting, simply because Elijah was so unsettled until he had been winded properly, and during the middle of the night, this really challenged me.

Winding aside, this whole "babies not putting on weight" thing is a common theme and I know that I am not alone with my experience. I've heard lots of stories of women being told in those first few days after birth that their milk is not good enough and that their babies are losing weight and may need to be topped with a bottle. It's crazy because babies lose weight after birth. That's a reality.

Given the time and encouragement, many women will go on to feed their babies perfectly adequately without the need for top ups. That's not all women; I appreciate that some are simply not able to establish breastfeeding – to this day, my mum is still sad that she was never able to breastfeed my brother and I beyond six weeks, simply because no one told her she needed to drink lots of water (and not milk, as she had been advised, and which she can't tolerate).

Others find that they don't have enough milk to satisfy the needs of their babies, or that they lose too much weight trying to sustain their milk supply due to the demands of the baby. Others simply don't have the energy, and others just don't like it. There are a myriad of reasons, and while I've always been very pro-breastfeeding, I do appreciate that it's not for everyone; it's a personal thing.

Successful breastfeeding

For me, once breastfeeding was established, that was it. I was well away and absolutely loved every minute of it. I loved the fact that I could nourish my son from my own body. There is this notion that the breasts constitute a chakra (energy centre) all of their own, and so when you're breastfeeding, you're not only physically and emotionally nourishing your baby (especially with you holding him/her by your heart space), but you're spiritually nourishing them too.

I also loved the fact that breastfeeding comforted and soothed Elijah. As mothers, we become experts on learning how to comfort and soothe our children. It's what we do best. You only have to see how a child calls out for his mum when he falls, and calms immediately when she picks him up and talks to him in soft tones, or how a baby calms immediately when he is brought to the breast, or rocked or "shh-ed". Well, Elijah was certainly calmed by my breast.

This certainly had its advantages, not least in helping him to settle to sleep, but also when we travelled. It was just so easy to whip out my boob on the aeroplane, for example, and not only calm him, but help to clear his ears as we changed altitude. He'd often sleep the whole journey. He was comforted by the boob on boats too, and made travel in that first year so easy. In fact, it made everything easy because we didn't need to faff around with bottles, or warming milk, and there it was, his source of nourishment within me.

Of course, this did present its challenges too. Elijah cluster fed for the first 16 weeks of his life. This meant that he was fussy each evening unless he was attached to my breast. No one really understands the reason that babies cluster feed, as it certainly didn't help Elijah to sleep through the night. But for whatever reason, he needed a constant supply of my milk during the evening, from approximately 6.30p.m. to 10.30p.m., when he'd finally fall asleep.

It was exhausting. In the earlier days, I had a really hard time accepting the fact that each evening, I basically had to sit down and feed him. Prior to the birth, I was used to teaching yoga each evening, and being out and about, and now, here I was, having little choice but to sit down and join E watching TV. I'm not a massive fan of TV so I tired of this novelty very quickly and became frustrated that I couldn't be doing something active instead.

I taught yoga again when Elijah was about six weeks old, and it was this that kept me sane. Yes, I was drained and often running on empty, and there is a very strong argument that post-natal yoga teachers should wait a good few months before giving to others through teaching, but I experience great joy from teaching; it stops me thinking about anything else and keeps me present.

However, I was a bit ambitious as I initially taught two evenings a week. This meant that E had a very testing time, because all Elijah wanted during those two hours was my breast. I had learned to express by then, but the bottle didn't cut it for Elijah, and I'd return home to a traumatised E and an unsettled baby. I'd take Elijah immediately to my breast and he'd calm down instantly, while E would pour himself an extra-large glass of wine!

Those evenings certainly didn't help our relationship at that time, and I soon cut back to just the one class a week. This, I absolutely relished, and it was a welcome break from the usual evening routine. Needless to say, we were both delighted when the cluster feeding finally came to an end and we could have some time together during the evening without Elijah attached to my breast!

Then, of course, there was the challenge of the night-time feeding, and nothing can prepare you for this. Initially, it was a novelty, and I had heard other women say that they spent that time watching TV and eating biscuits. So I tried this. As soon as Elijah awoke for a feed, I would take him downstairs and breastfeed while drinking tea, eating biscuits and watching TV. I quickly realised this approach was not for me and made me feel particularly yucky!

Instead, I stayed in bed and fed him there under the light of a lamp, while E continued to sleep beside me. I was OK with this initially, but after a few weeks of being woken every two to three hours, the sleep deprivation had truly kicked in, and I started getting resentful that E was able to sleep while I had to keep waking. It wasn't just the feeding, of course, but also the winding and the nappy changing that took the time.

I kept a little notebook by my bed and jotted down the time I was woken for feeding and the time I was able to go back to sleep again. The intention was to note how long Elijah was going between feeds, but really, all it did was make me completely obsessed by the number of hours of sleep I was getting each night, which wasn't very many at all. Sleep deprivation continues to be a major theme in my life, but more on that later.

Returning to work at 12 weeks certainly challenged the feeding schedule, as I had to ensure I had enough milk for my mum to be able to feed Elijah for me. There was so much work to do in the office, and while in the past, I had been able to work longer hours than I was contracted to do, now, I had to rush off at the contracted time to collect Elijah. I also had to make time to express milk, and I was often so busy that I had to make a real effort to factor this in.

Of course, my breasts made it very clear to me that it was feeding time, and I was certainly thrown into some degree of panic if I turned up at work having forgotten to put in my breast pads. Yikes, leaky breasts! Initially, expressing was challenging; I had invested in a double electric pump and I recall sitting at the kitchen table with one of my friends as I attempted to pump milk from my breasts. I felt like a milk cow and, with my friend laughing at me, it was perhaps hardly surprising that no milk came out!

My cousin suggested a handheld pump and that worked a treat. It also made it easy for me to express at work, as the only private space available to me was the toilets. This wasn't exactly ideal, but there really was no other option, so I just accepted my reality and I quickly established a routine, making sure to store the milk in the fridge and take it home with me at the end of the day.

Expressing soon became second nature, but it was another consideration in an already busy and exhausting day. I was increasingly frustrated at never really clearing my inbox and constantly chasing my tail. I was resentful of the fact I had to work and then rush straight to my parents to feed and collect Elijah. I then had to go home to the pile of washing and the cooking, and all the other chores that come with running a household.

I lived off 70% dark chocolate those weeks. And tea. And wine in the evening. I justified the chocolate on account of its iron content, and the fact I absolutely needed the caffeine and the sugar to get through the day. The wine I justified because the sugar from it was the only thing to get me through the evening and take the edge off a little bit. People say that you lose weight while you're breastfeeding, but with me, this certainly wasn't true. If anything, I put on weight, as I was constantly ravenous and totally thrown by this new way of being.

GOING PUBLIC

Initially, I had no qualms about breastfeeding in public, but then, we had an incident at six months that challenged this. E and I were on the neighbouring island of Jersey and had joined my Reiki Master and her husband for dinner at their local Indian restaurant. Elijah still liked to feed most of the early evening and so I spent much of that meal feeding him. I was wearing a floaty blouse, which made it easier – or so I thought – to breastfeed subtly in public.

Alas not. There was a couple sitting at the table next to us, the wife and I sat on the same bench that ran along the whole side of the restaurant. I was aware of their presence but I was so involved in our conversation that I didn't pay them too much attention. As they stood up to leave, the woman came over to talk to us. I was so used to people coming over and commenting on how beautiful Elijah was that I was confused by her words:

"It's disgusting the way you've breastfed that baby," she said.

"Sorry?" I asked, with a confused look on my face. "Sorry, what did you say?"

"I said it's disgusting the way you're breastfeeding that baby," she repeated.

I was startled. "Sorry," I heard myself saying, because this certainly wasn't what I was used to hearing, and it took me a moment to clock that, yes, she really did say those words, I hadn't misheard her and I wasn't imagining it. I never intended to upset someone else with my actions and so I was genuinely sorry, albeit totally confused.

By this point, E had stood up from his seat and was standing to the other side of the incensed, and drunken, lady.

"She's just feeding the baby," I heard E saying

"I nursed all of my children, but I would never have been as indiscreet as you," she said to me with disdain in her voice.

I was truly shocked. This had never happened previously, and while, yes, Elijah had been pretty much on and off my breast the whole time we were in the restaurant, I had been doing my best to manage this. Inevitably, there's always going to be a moment where you guide them on and off the nipple, and perhaps, by six months, I'd grown quite laidback about this, but heck, I was feeding my baby, it's a nipple, what's the big deal! Women sunbathe topless, for heaven's sake. It wasn't like I was sitting there, flaunting my breasts.

The lady was noticeably drunk and started challenging E, who was beginning to get a little wound up by this whole incident, which was something I'd never seen previously. He was most certainly my knight in shining armour that evening. The lady's husband had already left the restaurant and the restaurant staff quickly rushed over to see what was going on – I wasn't used to all this drama! I told E to let it go, which he did, and the lady quickly left the restaurant.

It was one of those horrible incidents that happened very quickly, but which has been ingrained on my memory ever since. The restaurant staff were incredibly friendly and apologetic, but of course, it wasn't their fault, and I was just confused by the whole experience and shaken for the rest of the evening.

Until that point, I'd never questioned breastfeeding in public. If Elijah needed feeding, I fed him; to me, it felt like the most natural thing in the world. But clearly, others didn't feel this way, and it saddens me that this is the case. I was annoyed I never got to find out exactly what element of me feeding Elijah upset the lady the most, so that I've never been able to make sense of the episode.

Unfortunately, I became less comfortable feeding in public after this, especially as Elijah grew older. If we were in a restaurant, I would take him off to the toilets to feed him, which was silly really, because who wants to eat their dinner in the toilets, poor Elijah! Or I'd faff around with scarves and muslins to hide the fact I was breastfeeding, and cause Elijah to get hot and stuffy instead.

NURSING STRIKE

Still, regardless of the negativity shown to me, my love affair with breastfeeding continued and I was therefore incredibly distraught when, at 10 months, Elijah went on a nursing strike. I was up in Edinburgh at the time, visiting one of my best friends. It was bedtime and I was feeding Elijah when he bit down hard on my nipple, causing it to bleed, and I yelped! And that was that.

It was the strangest thing, because that night, he didn't wake for a feed, which had never happened previously, and I awoke in anticipation, wondering if he was OK. The next morning, I considered that perhaps he'd just finally learned to sleep through, but alas not; he refused to take my breast. I googled it and was introduced to the concept of a nursing strike.

Later that day, flying back to Guernsey, he still refused to feed, and screamed his way back on the plane instead. It was frustrating, and incredibly upsetting, because ordinarily, he would have been comforted by breastfeeding. Back home, he still refused the breast. By now, my breasts were engorged, and I was incredibly emotional and teary. I wasn't ready to stop feeding, as it just felt far too sudden.

That evening, I approached the local Facebook breastfeeding group and was grateful for the advice. Someone suggested that Elijah might have an ear infection or some other condition that was putting him off feeding, so I took him to the doctor the next morning. The doctor thoroughly checked him over but couldn't find anything wrong with him and concluded that he'd simply decided that he didn't want to breastfeed anymore. There was a part of me that wasn't prepared to accept this, and I set out to do what I could to encourage him back to the breast again.

By then, I had researched "nursing strike" at length and I decided to put into practice my findings and the advice of other mothers who had experienced a similar thing. Thus, I did as much skin-to-skin as possible, laying naked with Elijah in the bath and in the bed. I woke during the night and brought him in his sleepy state to my breast to try to trick him into feeding again, and I tried not to be discouraged when he turned his head away from my nipple. I drew him to my breast again in the morning, determined not to give up, and later, on and off throughout the day. I kept expressing milk during this time to maintain my flow and ease the pressure in my breasts.

Finally, during the fifth night, after days of tears, skin-to-skin, and expressing, he took to my breast again. The nursing strike was over. It was very early in the morning and I was so delighted and excited that I woke E to share my good news with him. It was such a relief and I couldn't have been happier; my son wanted to breastfeed again! I loved the intimacy of it, and the connection it created, and it made me appreciate the beauty of breastfeeding in a way I had perhaps taken for granted previously. E didn't really understand and would have been happy if Elijah had stopped feeding when he was six months old, as others do.

LONGER-TERM BREASTFEEDING

E was desperately uncomfortable with the idea of me breastfeeding Elijah until the two years I intended, and my dad also had a similar opinion on the matter. But I was determined, as I felt there were many benefits to be gained. Admittedly, the accompanying sleep deprivation was challenging, but I knew it was beneficial for strengthening his immune system and providing him with a natural immunity, plus, of course, the emotional, mental and spiritual benefits too.

I resisted the pressure I was experiencing from E and other people's negativity, because deep down, I knew it was the right decision for Elijah and me. It helped that my best mummy friend was also breastfeeding her son, and in fact, continued to do so as she became pregnant with her second son. Both of us would talk at length about the need to wean at some stage, more so because we were both exhausted by the night-time feeding, but the trouble was, neither of us really knew how to do this.

As it happened, her son weaned himself. Apparently, when you are pregnant, the taste of your milk can change and her son didn't like it. In so doing, she proved our theory, that the breastfeeding was causing the excess night waking, because her son started sleeping much better. Elijah, on the other hand was still, 18 months in, waking every two to three hours. It was getting super draining.

I was in a quandary. I had a sense that I wanted to breastfeed for two years. As I mentioned earlier, I loved the intimacy of it and, furthermore, I knew it was doing him good. The World Health Organization believes that breastfeeding is the normal way of providing young infants with the nutrients they need for healthy growth and development. They recommend exclusive breastfeeding up to six months of age, with continued breastfeeding along with appropriate complementary foods up to two years of age and beyond.

Research has shown that breast milk provides key nutrients well beyond the first year of life, especially protein, fat and most vitamins. Research has also shown that breastmilk boosts the immune system. Babies who are breastfed have decreased incidences of illness and lower mortality rates. The immunity benefits improve the longer a baby breastfeeds and the less likely they are to have some of the illnesses that are associated with not breastfeeding, like ear infections and upper respiratory infections. Certainly, Elijah was rarely ill and never required antibiotics. I also felt strongly that his immune system should be allowed to develop naturally without being injected with any foreign bodies or unnecessary pharmaceutical drugs, which don't work with the body.

Extended breastfeeding is meant to make the mother healthier too and reduce her risk of breast cancer, ovarian cancer and endometrial cancer. I was keen to do all I could to reduce the negative effects of the IVF drugs in increasing my risk of contracting ovarian and endometrial cancer particularly.

Studies have also shown that breastfeeding helps boost brain development in babies, and that's not just from nutrients. By moving the baby from one breast to the other (unlike bottle-feeding, where the baby is often held in the same position at each feed), and put into different positions, the baby is given the opportunity to look and reach in different directions and exercise his/her mind.

As proven by Elijah time and time again, breastfeeding is also soothing and can help to calm an infant in a stressful situation. It's also calming for the mother and provides the mother with an opportunity to sit down and connect with her child, everything else having to wait. In this way, it can also increase intimacy and provide the positive knock-on effect that this alone has on the health and wellbeing of both the mother and the baby. Certainly, this has always been very important to me.

So while I may well have been tired from the constant (or so it felt at times!) night-time feeding demands, I was adamant that I didn't want to stop breastfeeding (and extended breastfeeding), and this is something I am very passionate about, but I was feeling the pressure from E and other family members to stop.

Furthermore, I was aware that we had one frozen blastocyst and two frozen embryos in Southampton, and for as long as I could remember, I had wanted to have two children, so at some point I was going to need to do something about it. The trouble was, we were both tired, and the thought of going through the baby stage and the sleep deprivation all over again didn't fill E or I with much joy, and I was still breastfeeding my first-born.

E wasn't even sure that he wanted to have another child, and we had a period of disagreement about this. While I wasn't overly happy about having to put my body through IVF again, I was keen to give Elijah a sibling – someone once said to me that the greatest gift you can give your son or daughter is a sibling, and this has certainly been my experience in that my brother, Ross, and I have grown up extremely close to one another.

Admittedly, Ross and I fought together as children, but as we grew older, we became firm friends. We even went to universities near to one another and we bought a house together in our mid-twenties, which we sold to pay for us each to go travelling. Heck, we even went to our first yoga class together, and both trained as yoga teachers in Byron Bay, albeit with different teachers. Ross is still living out there today, having met his Australian fiancée on their yoga teacher training course, and the rest is history!

So I know only too well how much of a joy it can be to have a sibling in your life and I was keen for Elijah to experience this. E is one of three and, while he adores his siblings, he still needed to undertake some research to determine whether he really did want to have another child. He did this in the same way that enabled him to make the decision to try for Elijah in the first place, by talking to his trusted friends. Being older, they'd all had multiple children by this point and were keen to encourage him to do the same – well, to have another one at least!

Eventually, after a few months of mulling it over, he agreed, with some resignation, that yes, we should try again for another baby. He, like me, didn't like the idea of essentially letting the embryos go to waste without giving them a chance at life. The only issue was that there is never a good time for this. I was aware that at the six-week check-up with my doctor, I'd said "never again", but the human brain is marvellous in that it forgets how difficult things can be, plus the female body is often wired to feel a deep yearning for a baby, even if the mind is putting up a little resistance.

By this time, I was fast approaching my 40th birthday and I was feeling the pressure of my age, and also the fact that Elijah was now 17 months old and I didn't want there to be a huge gap between the children. So I was aware that if we truly wanted to try for another baby then we needed to get on with it. I figured that we'd celebrate my birthday in style and then I'd nestle down and prepare my body for another round of IVF

Only, that I still wasn't quite sure how I was going to stop breastfeeding and wean Elijah, at least in a gentle way, as you are not meant to do IVF if you are breastfeeding. So I did the one thing I knew I could do – I handed it over to the angels and prayed for a solution.

PART 5

Another Round of IVF

Chapter 22

A Frozen Embryo Cycle

Once my 40th birthday was celebrated, I felt a pressure – admittedly my own – to try another round of IVF and use one of the three frozen embryos (one of which was a blastocyst) stored at the clinic in Southampton. It was July and Elijah was due to turn two in the November, and I was aware that time was ticking and we weren't getting any younger; E was 48 years old, approaching his 49th birthday just after Elijah's birthday in the November.

The miracle of science means that embryos can be frozen in time and thawed for use in future cycles, depending on their quality. This is called a frozen cycle and means that you have to take medication to prevent ovulation and to prepare the uterus for embryo transfer. Once the endometrium (lining of the uterus) is of the right thickness, further medication is introduced and the thawing process takes place.

The embryos are thawed in the laboratory and assessed as to whether they have fully survived the thawing process. Sometimes, embryos don't survive the thawing process, or aren't of a good enough quality to be used, and if this happens then there is little that can be done, aside from meet with one of the consultants to discuss further options – the success rate differs from one clinic to another and depends on all sorts of factors, such as the stage of development the embryos were at when they were frozen, and the effect of freezing on the different embryos. Wessex find that approximately 80% of frozen embryos survive the freezing/thawing process.

I have always appreciated that there are no guarantees with IVF, but I was feeling desperately uncomfortable with the thought that you could take a whole heap of medication to get your body ready to receive an embryo, only for the embryo to die during the thawing process, or not be of a good enough quality to be used in that particular IVF cycle.

It was for this reason that I decided I would continue breastfeeding, despite the fact that breastfeeding is a big "no-no" in the IVF world. I had spent months deliberating about this and had even discussed this with my counsellor to help me make a decision, so it was not a decision that I'd taken lightly.

I read extensively on the subject and took much comfort in the fact that I was not alone. Many women go through the breastfeeding/IVF quandary, and with good reason. For many, this may be their only chance to breastfeed, as there are no guarantees that IVF will work for them again.

Furthermore, while the clinics insist that you stop, due to the potential harmful effect on the breastfed toddler or child, there is little research or evidence to quantify this, as it would be unethical to obtain it. The concern is more over the effect that breastfeeding may have on a woman's hormonal status and the manner in which this may impact upon the effectiveness of the IVF drugs in controlling the woman's hormonal status.

Like most women in my position, I was effectively hedging my bets. It's not an easy decision to make, and I was judged for it. But at the end of the day, right, or wrong, it was the decision that I felt most comfortable with for all concerned, and E supported me with it.

On day one of my menstrual cycle, I arranged a set-up appointment via telephone with a nurse at Wessex, to run through the process. There were lots of forms for both E and I to complete, and I had to have another HIV test as my previous one had expired. This was slightly annoying, as it was yet another IVF expense, although the frozen embryo cycle was going to cost us significantly less than the first cycle, at £1,270 for the treatment and then £53 per set of blood tests (I would need two to three of these); the costs of the additional HIV test and the cost of the travel and accommodation, meant that all in all it would cost approximately £2,100.

I also had to attend MSG in Guernsey to be reminded how to inject myself and to pick up my prescription for the drugs. My heart felt heavy and I couldn't get excited like I had done on the first attempt. I didn't really want to be injecting myself with all the drugs, and I felt the self-pity seeping in before I'd even begun.

I was very well aware that IVF is hard work. It demands mental, emotional and physical strength, and I was already tired. The constant sleepless nights had taken their toll, plus, our lifestyle hadn't slowed down at all. It was the summer, and the summer is active in nature, and I was active with it. I didn't know how to stop, or to get to bed early, or to do any of those things that I knew I should do to encourage a more restful state of being.

I also hadn't really prepared myself, beyond reducing my wine consumption and eating as healthily as I could. I was still practicing yoga, but not in a manner that might support the IVF. I didn't seem to have the time to meditate or to practice Yoga Nidra, as I had done previously, and anyway, the Sankalpa, "I am pregnant with a healthy baby", felt forced and didn't resonate anymore.

Furthermore, while I went for a few acupuncture sessions, I did this because I felt that I had to, and even then, it was tricky finding the time, and I would rush in and out to get on with whatever else I had scheduled into my busy days. I certainly didn't manage to find the time to go for reflexology and Reiki sessions; having a toddler in my life and a busy job certainly challenged this.

The drugs

With a frozen cycle, you need to take a whole cocktail (or so it felt) of drugs to go through the process of suppression. This temporarily shuts down the ovaries and prevents any eggs from being released. Remember, we already had three embryos (one at blastocyst stage) so we didn't need to go through the stimulation of the ovaries or egg collection.

Fortunately, we were given another treatment booklet, as we had been given during the first antagonist cycle to conceive Elijah. This time, the booklet detailed the process for a GEEP Cycle. GEEP stands for GNRH Exogenous Estrogen and Progesterone, and essentially means that drugs are used to prepare the body to receive the thawed embryo. This involved the use of more drugs than during the antagonist cycle, and I was grateful that each step of the treatment plan was detailed in the booklet and this time, tailored for those of us from Guernsey too.

The treatment schedule began in earnest on the 19th day of my cycle, and with that, I started a seven-day course of Provera. This is a synthetic form of progesterone, which the clinic uses to suppress the natural cycle so that they can then control it through drugs. It's a tablet, which felt strong on my liver, and I wasn't best pleased about having my cycle suppressed like this.

I am fascinated by women's cycles and the manner in which these can be so insightful about how we are living our lives and our mental, emotional and spiritual state of being. We have a womb wisdom, and I wasn't sure I liked my womb being artificially manipulated like this. I had a level of resistance to the process, and angst about what was happening to my body, yet I knew I had little choice if I wanted to have another baby.

On the 21st day of that same cycle, I had to start injecting the drug Buserelin before 11a.m. each morning. Buserelin is a synthetic form of a hormone that occurs naturally in the body. It works by acting on the pituitary gland in the brain to stop the production of natural hormones that control the release of eggs from the ovaries. E administered the injections for me and I tried my best to just suck it up again and accept my reality, but I quickly grew weary of the drug regime.

Ten days later, my period started, and four days after that, I had to attend MSG for a blood test. It was such a relief that this testing could be done in Guernsey and that I didn't need to travel to Southampton. The test checks the levels of the hormone oestrogen in your blood to see whether suppression of the natural cycle has occurred, meaning that your system is essentially shut down so that you do not release an egg.

Fortunately, I was suitably supressed, and with that, we were now able to move to the GEEP cycle. It really felt like a long and drawn-out treatment schedule, as I had been taking drugs for 15 days at that point, and was now about to begin a new cycle of the treatment plan.

This cycle involved a reduction in the dosage of the Buserelin, although this still needed to be injected daily. Also, I now had to start Progynova, oestrogen tablets that prepare the endometrium for implantation of the embryo I had to take 2 mg dosage for five days, before the dosage was increased to 4 mg for four days, and then up to 6 mg for the remainder of the treatment.

On the 15th day of the GEEP cycle, I began taking the Cyclogest pessaries twice a day too. Cyclogest contains the active ingredient progesterone, which acts on the lining of the uterus and causes it to thicken in preparation for a fertilised egg to implant. On the basis that pregnancy occurs, this medication is continued until the placenta develops fully and begins to produce progesterone, to continue to support the pregnancy.

This meant that, each morning, I was now injecting Buserelin and taking 2 mg of Progynova and 400 mg of Cyclogest. At lunchtime, I had to take an additional 2 mg of Progynova, and then in the evening, I took the last 2 mg of the Progynova, and also an additional 400 mg of the Cyclogest. While inserting a pessary into the vagina twice a day is not ideal, at least it bypassed the liver, so that was one less thing to process.

On the 17th day of the GEEP cycle, I had to attend Southampton for a blood test, with the possibility of embryo transfer a few days later. It wasn't ideal timing, as this coincided with a pre-booked yoga course with Cyndi Lee in London, which I was due to attend with a friend.

This meant having to tell my friend what was happening, which was unfortunate as we had hoped to keep the IVF a secret, not only to make it more intimate, but to reduce the pressure. Furthermore, while I tried to convince myself that a yoga course was the ideal environment for an embryo to take root, rushing up to London with family now in tow was likely going to challenge that.

NOT IN THE RIGHT MENTAL ZONE

We also now had two days between the blood test and embryo transfer to fill, and I felt this overwhelming and all-encompassing need to go to Glastonbury. We'd visited briefly when Elijah was three months old, and something about the energy of the place had gotten under my skin. I knew I needed to return.

They say that Glastonbury is the heart chakra of the world and home of the Mother Goddess. It is located where the St Michael and St Mary ley lines meet and has an incredibly healing and nurturing energy. As a result of this energy, it attracts spiritual seekers and those connecting to the other worlds. For me, it feels a little like coming home.

It wasn't until we were in Glastonbury, however, that I realised how much I needed its energy and its healing. This was validated to me on the eve of embryo transfer when I went for an Angel Reiki session with a practitioner in the centre of town. I'd not come across Angel Reiki until then, and I'm not entirely sure how it differs from Usui Reiki, which is the traditional Reiki that I practice. From what I gather, the attunement for Angelic Reiki comes from the Angels rather than through a Reiki Master like me. This means that the Angelic Reiki has not been affected by the consciousness of the Reiki Master as it comes quite literally from the purity of the Angels directly.

When booking the session, I hadn't realised that the lady practiced Angelic Reiki, I just assumed she was Usui trained, and I had to trust that whatever brought me to her was in the highest good for all concerned. That said, I wasn't so sure about the angelic approach, as the energy felt very light. Still, I managed to drift off to that liminal space between awake and asleep, which brings with it the opportunity for healing and rest, which was the important thing.

The lady commented that I wasn't in the here and now, floating in the ether instead. She was right, I was aware that I had been ungrounded and disconnected since the trauma of the placenta previa, two years before.

The lady knew that I was undertaking IVF and I knew that she knew that there wasn't a soul waiting to come in. How could it, as I had no grounding or anchoring to draw it in. It was a desperately uncomfortable feeling, and I didn't like that she could see my truth so clearly through the layers of denial I'd created to try to keep me safe (an illusion!).

It felt strange being in the centre of Glastonbury town that afternoon, as I felt as if I was floating through it, and I saw others floating through it too. I was deeply aware that what we put out is reflected back to us, and I was uncomfortable seeing so many lost souls wandering around. I couldn't keep pretending that all was well, and there was a painful recognition that I, too, was fragmented and disconnected to my soul.

Walking up Glastonbury Tor later that afternoon, I wondered whether I had been drawn to Glastonbury to ground me ahead of the embryo transfer, as if I might wing it at the last minute. It's a ridiculous thought really, as you don't just "wing" IVF. There was no chance of that, regardless, as I continued to self-sabotage into the evening, drinking some wine with a particularly spicy meal, which, I'm very well aware, imbalances my energy.

A part of me was hugely resisting the IVF process, because deep down, in my heart of hearts, I knew that I wasn't ready. How could I be? I wasn't sure who I was and what I wanted anymore.

It was a fascinating experience, as it gave me a real insight into the concept of manifestation and how we absolutely need to feel mentally aligned, and how we need to feel deep within, with every ounce of our being, the need for whatever it is we're trying to create and bring in (manifest in form).

I certainly wasn't feeling it. I felt like a fraud, praying for a healthy pregnancy, because this wasn't my truth, so I prayed for other things instead, things that seemed more pressing, and which had nothing to do with the IVF process.

The next day, we returned to Southampton for embryo transfer. We had arranged for my dad to fly over from

Guernsey for the day to look after Elijah while we attended the clinic. It wasn't that the clinic had said we couldn't take him with us, more so that they had not been encouraging of it, and we felt it should be an intimate affair, without having to manage him.

However, it was far from intimate. We didn't know the consultant or the nurse, and we felt a lack of connection to either. The embryologist explained that they had thawed the two remaining embryos, leaving the blastocyst frozen. Of the embryos, one had not survived the thawing process, and the other one, they had managed to culture to blastocyst stage.

This threw me a little, as I had expected to use the blastocyst frozen at the time Elijah was conceived, but the clinic felt that we should use the recently cultured one instead as this was now awaiting implantation (the blastocyst frozen from Elijah's cycle remained frozen).

The embryologist showed us an example image of the blastocyst we would be using to demonstrate the quality of it, and explained that it was of slightly less quality than the one we had in storage, but that the difference was miniscule.

However, that miniscule difference meant a lot to me and I knew then and there that it wasn't going to result in a pregnancy. It didn't help that we had trouble identifying the image of the star of the blastocyst on the screen as it was released into my uterus, as we had so clearly seen when the blastocyst that became Elijah was released into my uterus. It just all felt like such a clinical procedure that was over within minutes.

Joining my dad and Elijah for lunch in a park near to the clinic, I could certainly feel the expansive energy of the new life within me, and I shall always be grateful for that opportunity. However, over the weekend, while on the yoga course in London, I struggled to feel it, and knew it wasn't going to make it.

I'd known for a while that I needed to experience a failed IVF cycle, to know how it felt to be a more empathic healer and yoga teacher. A number of women who have experienced failed cycles, have come to me for Reiki and yoga and it was difficult for me to understand exactly what they were going through, having not gone through it myself previously. I just had a sense that it was important that I had a clear and embodied understanding of this, of what it feels like to fail a cycle, for my own learning, empathy and ability to help others.

Working with some of these other women, I could feel in their energy that there was some resistance to the process and that there was a lack of grounding, faith and trust in the process and in their ability to create new life in this world. I also had a sense that the IVF was part of their journey towards greater healing and connection to self. Fertility issues, and the need for medical assistance through IVF had arisen in their life as an opportunity to go deeper, to do the inner work required to truly "know thyself", and to connect, perhaps for the first time, or more deeply then, with their spirituality and the spiritual element of all life.

Perhaps here too, I was being encouraged to dig a bit deeper and know myself a little more intimately too. During our first attempt at IVF, I had come to recognise how the process had increased my faith in, and connection to, Source, and encouraged me to drop into the space that supported this. My practise had deepened and awakened me to the potential to heal myself and know my own truth. It had been an empowering experience in manifestation, too.

Here, now, I knew there was more healing work to be done. I was quite literally sitting on an awful lot of anger and frustration in my pelvis. My faith had been challenged with the placenta previa and the taxing introduction to motherhood, and I knew that I needed to make peace with this before truly inviting another soul into this world.

Still, this awareness didn't make the 12-day waiting period to take the pregnancy test any the less challenging. It was awful. I slept fitfully, waking with this frantic need to feel the energy of the embryo within me. And even though, deep down, I knew that the IVF wasn't working, there was still a level of denial that had me trying to convince myself that I could feel the energy.

The days passed slowly and I spent a lot of time with my hands on my lower tummy, feeling anxious and daunted. Fear had taken root and I couldn't seem to shift it.

I'm not sure I really slept the night before taking the test. By 5a.m., I'd definitely had enough and took myself off to the bathroom, shaking with the apprehension. This time, I didn't bother to take the test through to E, I just left it sitting on the edge of the bath while I went downstairs to put the kettle on and make a cup of tea. By the time I returned, the test was complete, and there it was, validating what I already knew, "Not pregnant". And with that, I burst into tears.

Chapter 23

Recovering From a Failed IVF Cycle

Failing an IVF cycle sucks. It's not so much the wasted time and money, nor the fact you've pumped medication into your body unnecessarily, but it's the loss of the life you began to allow yourself to imagine. Broken dreams. And the fact that on some level, you feel that you're not good enough to be blessed with the gift of new life, almost as if the Universe has it in for you.

I knew that I needed to understand how a failed IVF cycle felt to be a more empathetic, conscious and compassionate healer, and be able to help others, but it still hurt. Having already had Elijah undoubtedly softened the blow, and I can only imagine how much tougher it must be for those couples who have not already been blessed with a baby. Furthermore, I cannot imagine having to go through failed cycles repeatedly.

Deep down, I had known the IVF was not going to work, and I'd self-sabotaged really, but this didn't stop me from feeling shocked. It was my wake-up call and it was E's wake-up call too. He'd been going through the motions with me, but not feeling it either, concerned as he was whether we would cope with another baby, with both of us still so sleep deprived by the first.

We processed the failing in our own way, and both concluded that actually, yes, we really did want another baby. As I mentioned earlier, we'd been told the greatest gift we could give Elijah was a sibling, and we both felt this. We were older parents with siblings of our own living, for the most part, the other side of the world, and we didn't want Elijah being left alone.

We were also very well aware that we only had one frozen blastocyst still remaining, stored as it was in the clinic in Southampton. We knew this was our last chance, because we didn't want to have to go through the whole process from the beginning again; it was this blastocyst or it was none.

I still recall the moment in the clinic during embryo transfer the first time, when two of the three blastocysts had been inserted into my uterus, and we were told that the remaining blastocyst would be frozen. I had this overwhelming sense that the blastocyst would become a baby one day. It had concerned me slightly, as I didn't want to have three children, believing at that point that I may have twins.

However, they say that the Universe only gives you as much as you can handle, and clearly, we weren't going to be able to manage twins, as only one of the blastocysts took. And now, here we were, hoping to try for a second baby, and only having that one frozen blastocyst still available to us.

It's a strange concept; a life conceived with the energy of a February full moon in 2013 and yet frozen in time for use in another year, 2016 to be exact, and the way things were looking, it would be March for implantation, the same month that it had been during that first cycle in 2013.

I knew now, with absolute certainty, that I wanted this frozen blastocyst to become a baby. I also knew that to achieve this, I needed to make changes. My body felt acidic and exhausted, my mind was cluttered and agitated, my spirit had been flagging, and my life had grown too busy and noisy. I recognised that it was time to retreat, heal, deepen my faith, and get my feet firmly back down on the ground again.

ANOTHER TRY

It was October 2015 at the time and I had a follow-up telephone call with the clinic, confirming that I wanted to try again, using our final blastocyst. The consultant was happy for me to begin whenever I felt ready, and I had a feeling that this would be in the following February, with implantation in

March. I was keen to align the frozen embryo cycle as closely as possible with the original cycle, and give myself plenty of time to heal.

The seasons each have their own energy, encouraging a different way of being; you can see this clearly in nature. As I've mentioned earlier spring is full of the incredible vibrancy of new life and new beginnings, ignited by Imbolc on 1st February, and I wanted to tap into this. I felt that to thaw the blastocyst in the same seasonal energy that it was frozen would spark some recognition, and there would be a resonance that would be lacking at other times of the year.

Furthermore, nature encourages one to retreat, rejuvenate and replenish during the darker months of the year, and I was keen to flow with this. The timing felt "right", as if it was always meant to be.

And I suspect it was always meant to be, for it felt as if my decision-making caused a rush of support to come in. I asked the angels for help and help was given.

I got this overwhelming feeling that I needed to go and see my Ayurvedic doctor, and on her recommendation, and with complete ease, I booked myself on a three-day Panchakarma at her clinic near Gatwick during the beginning of December.

This was a deeply healing experience, not least the opportunity to spend two nights on my own, and much of it in silence, but the effect of the treatments too. I was massaged within an inch of my life, my body nourished and my mind cooled and quietened with the use of glorious oils and herbs, and my soul nurtured and brought back to life. Energetically, my feet also came back into contact with the earth again and I grounded down.

There was another benefit to the trip, in that Elijah self-weaned. He was two by then and I had been praying for a peaceful weaning experience, and lo and behold, it came. My Ayurvedic doctor had been keen for me to wean him to support my own health, and had proposed the use of herbs, which would make my milk taste bitter.

It had taken me a while to come to terms with this, and reach the point where I felt ready to do so. Thus, I agreed to the herbs being massaged around my nipples during the treatment. Whether Elijah could sense the change in my smell, or had decided himself that he was ready to wean, I'll never know, but strangely, he didn't even try to feed upon my return. I admit I grieved for a few days, but I was welcoming of the shift this created for the family.

I'll also admit that Elijah started sleeping better, and he woke only every three hours compared to the two hours he had been waking previously. The trouble was, I couldn't pacify him with my breast anymore, although I quickly discovered that a cuddle seemed to do the job, and I spent much of the night cuddling him now instead. This didn't seem so bad, plus, I started to feel like I had a little more energy, and I enjoyed the additional freedom – E could now try settling Elijah to sleep (this was the bit that often took the time and energy!).

I also went for some Ki massage sessions with a very intuitive and gifted healer, Jo de Diepold Braham who helped me to recognise and come to terms with the anger and rage I had been holding in my uterus towards the placenta previa and the caesarean section. These sessions were insightful and taught me more about how we hold our emotions in the physical body, and how this affects how we feel on every other level too, and the manner in which our lives unfold in the material world as a result of this.

I also finally managed to find an ornament for my altar of a family of four, so I had a clear visual of what I was trying to create – I'd been looking for one of these for months and without success until then. I updated my vision board too, with images of babies and me pregnant, something I hadn't done for the failed cycle.

MENTALLY PREPARING

New Year arrived, and with that, I did a burning bowl ceremony. This is where you write down on a piece of paper all that you don't want to bring into your life in the new year, so all the things you want to let go of – it might be a person, a behavioural pattern, a habit or anything else for that matter that is no longer serving you. Then you burn the paper in a bowl, letting it go into the ether. After you've done your letting go, you've essentially made space for the "new" to come into your life. To do this, you initially express gratitude for all that you already have in your life. Feeling gratitude in the body helps to attract more of the good stuff in ("gratitude turns what we have into enough and more").

You then take a piece of paper, write your name on it and list your intentions for the year, but write them as if they had already happened, so in the present tense, for example, "I am pregnant with a healthy baby", rather than "I would like to be pregnant". It's important to really feel it in your body, whatever it is you're trying to bring in, and to feel a sense of gratitude for this too.

You then pop the paper in an envelope and put it away to read at the end of the year, leaving the Universe to work its magic, with you open to this potential – this is also important, you have to believe in your intentions, just as you have to believe in your dreams for them to come true! If you're Reiki attuned then you can channel Reiki onto the envelope to empower your intentions even further.

I often hold a burning bowl ceremony at the end of the year for Guernsey yoga students. We come together not only to write down the things we want to let go of, but we try to let go of them through our yoga practice too, having a feel for where the "stuff" (people, behaviour pattern, etc.) is held in our bodies, be that the tension in our shoulders or the pain in our hips, and trying to release this with a combination of awareness, movement and the breath.

At the beginning of the New Year, a few days after the burning bowl ceremony, we come together again to set our intentions, trying to embody them through our yoga practice, by feeling them in the body, and feeling a sense of gratitude for all we already have in our lives. I collect up the letters sealed as they are in self-addressed envelopes, and channel Reiki onto them before popping them away in a drawer for a year. I then send them out to the students at the end of the year causing quite a surprise as many have by then forgotten about their letters!

So here I was at the end of 2015 doing my own little ceremony (I'm a solitary practitioner!), in the peace of my yoga space, in front of the altar, with candles and incense burning, trying to usher in the magic that accompanies these rituals. Here, I let go of the old, burning the paper in my singing bowl, before expressing gratitude for all I already had in my life, especially my boys, E and Elijah, and establishing my intentions for the year ahead. This bit was easy as 2016 was all about creation, not least getting back to writing again (a passion that I had stopped when Elijah was born) and bringing another soul into the world, Amen ("so be it").

I truly believe that once an intention has been set and is felt deep within one's heart and soul, then a spark ignites in the ether and the Universe conspires to provide the support that is needed to assist you on your journey. All you've got to do is get out of your own way and try not to control the process – the ego is so limited in comparison to the potential of spirit and grace.

It was poignant, therefore, that two weeks later, I cracked some ribs while skiing my last run of the skiing holiday. I quickly realised the reason that it had happened because it hurt to move, which meant I couldn't really do anything. I had needed to slow down, and the Universe had intervened and made sure of that! The Universe leaves signs and prompts to direct you along the path, but if you continue to ignore them and not listen to the advice that is given, then it will take drastic action to get your attention.

The Universe had my attention and I almost laughed at the state I now found myself in. I had little choice but to rest. I couldn't exercise and I couldn't practice yoga, at least not in the active manner I had been practicing previously. It was a blessing really, as it encouraged me out of my denial and into a whole new way of being, especially on my yoga mat.

Thus it now presented me with the opportunity to practice restorative yoga, which I had not practiced for years. This was perfect, as it helped me to acknowledge the depths of my exhaustion and to (finally) do something about this. I was amazed how quickly I felt the benefits of resting in poses for prolonged periods of time, and I am thankful to Judith Lasater's book, *Relax and Renew*, for guidance on this.

I also dropped into my Yoga Nidra space again and soon felt aligned with the Sankalpa, "I am pregnant with a healthy baby". I was meditating again too, and I prayed for a successful IVF cycle and asked for the support and guidance of the angels. I invested in rose quartz and moonstone, both reputed to assist with fertility and pregnancy, and got my fertility bracelet fixed after the string broke. I also dowsed for the Bach floral remedies to support me.

By the February, I was feeling more myself again. I was much stronger both physically and mentally than I had been for some time, and my faith and connection to Source felt restored. I also felt empowered, as I had listened to my intuition and the guidance of the Universe, and tried my best to flow with both, and now, here I was, feeling whole and centred again; healed then.

I knew I was now ready for another round of IVF and I had a strong sense that this time the treatment would result in a positive outcome. It was a relief, I was back in my IVF zone and focused on doing all I could to support and trust in the process; bring it on!

Chapter 24

Another Frozen Embryo Cycle

I can't tell you what a difference a few months made in aligning me fully to the IVF process. It was a huge lesson for me. There is a timing for everything and you cannot rush these things. You absolutely cannot afford to have any resistance to the treatment either.

I was absolutely not ready in October. I was not aligned in any way, and there was a good deal of underlying resistance. I was doing what I thought I should be doing, rather than what I felt I should do. I was fearful of time rushing away and unfulfilled dreams, and because of this, it lacked grounding; there was no connection to the Universe, I was misreading signs, and was full of fear rather than excitement.

Life was very different now. It was February 2016 and I felt truly committed to fulfilling my New Year's intention of bringing new life into the world. I was ready. I was excited. The timing felt right, this time of year and IVF had a meaning to it for me.

We decided that we wouldn't tell anyone, not even our parents, so that it could be our own special journey, E and I. This made a huge difference, as it gave the experience more intimacy. I also made it known that I was retreating a little from the world, to focus on a creative writing project, but of course, there were two creative projects going on, and the significance of this – at least energetically, emotionally and spiritually – was crucial for me. It was a time to create.

Incidentally, a creative writing project was also very significant here because it brought back to life a manuscript that I had almost given up on, that I had written nine years earlier, before I had met E. It had been playing on my mind for some time and I was desperate to embrace my more creative side, so I hoped that in bringing this back into my life, and trying to tap into my creative side, it would have a positive effect in creating a new baby in my life too…

The cycle

The frozen embryo cycle was identical to the one we had followed in October. The only difference was the fact we paid an additional amount (approximately £150) for embryo glue, which is meant to help the embryo implant in the uterus. This hadn't been offered to us in the other cycle, or at least I hadn't been aware it was an option that we could elect to use.

In terms of drugs, there we were again; day 19 of my cycle on 8th February 2016 and I started a seven-day course of the oral Provera so that my cycle could be controlled once more. Two days later, the injecting began. Twelve days after that, I had a blood test to determine that my body was responding to the drugs positively. Six days after that, we started the GEEP cycle, which involved the Progynova tablets.

I recognised the need to retreat from the world and immerse myself in the healing power of nature during the beginning of treatment, and to give it the attention it deserved. Thus, the three of us retreated to stay in a cosy cottage on the peaceful, small island of Herm together for four days in the depths of winter, turning off the Wi-Fi.

I run bi-annual Yoga and Wellbeing retreats on Herm island, and for good reason – it's the most perfect place to retreat! Measuring only 1.5 miles in length by 0.5 miles in width, it's really not very big, and this means it has no cars and no bicycles, making it a delightful environment to just "be". It's also very easy for us to access the island, as it's only located three miles from Guernsey and involves a 20-minute ferry journey, and yet, it's a whole world away.

We spent our days walking around the island, immersed in its natural beauty, with its unspoilt beaches and stunning views of the other Channel Islands and the French coastline in the distance. It's a haven for birds and we enjoyed watching these, while embracing the solitude of the island at this time of year – even the pub was closed! We also swam in the freezing cold sea and scavenged for "treasure" along the empty beaches, hearing the cries of the oyster catchers, and the wind blowing the cobwebs away.

We managed to get Elijah into a good napping pattern and while he slept, I practised yoga on my own, enjoying the views of the sea and the island of Alderney, from my yoga space in the cottage. Here, I spent time resting, with my legs up the wall, channelling Reiki onto my womb space.

Our trip to Herm was a special time and ensured that we were truly in the intimate IVF zone for the rest of the treatment. It was now just a matter of continuing with this, and as I did so, my connection to the Divine deepened and my faith was restored.

So, by the time we got to embryo transfer, I was really excited. It was due to happen a few days after my March Yoga and Wellbeing retreat also on Herm, and that whole weekend just felt perfect in terms of preparing me; not least the energy of Herm again and immersing myself in that beautiful yogic energy with other like-minded souls, but also the opportunity to swim in the sea and connect to nature over the weekend.

It seemed that every time we left the room we were staying in, there was a robin up in the tree by the side of the steps leading down to the pathway below. As mentioned earlier, robins are angels in disguise and also serve as validation that life is about to change – I love how the Universe provides signs in nature, and our job is just to notice and interpret these signs. Birds, for example, all have different meanings, you just need to google whatever you're seeing: "metaphysical reason for seeing…"

The robin was most certainly a sign and I took great comfort in this. So too on the way to the airport, a few days later, when an owl flew right in front of the car at dusk. It was such a random occurrence that even E was blown away by the coincidence. Yes, there was no doubt that the time was right. The owl is representative of mystery, magic, vision and guidance, and is one of the most ancient signs for spirit contact. Owls alert you to the spirit activity around you, and I was certainly feeling it.

It's not a feeling that happens often, but when it does, it's very special because it brings with it a sense that everything is connected and that you are being fully supported by the Universe. I believe that Reiki heightens this feeling, increasing synchronicity and coincidence, as if pieces of the jigsaw of life suddenly piece together and the picture becomes clearer. All of a sudden you start to see the signs all over the place; for example, books fall off shelves, you meet someone who knows someone who can help you solve a problem or move your life forward, you keep hearing the same song on the radio or you see the same advert three times. This is the key – noticing that you're seeing the same things repeatedly!

As with our previous GEEP cycle, there was always the risk that the embryo – or in this case, the six-day-old blastocyst, which had been frozen for three years now – may not survive the thawing process, and that the seven weeks of medication might have been in vain. But fortunately for us, this was not the case, the blastocyst survived and I felt that it had been waiting patiently for us this whole time.

Feeling positive

E and I flew to Southampton together that evening. It was the first time we had left Elijah with my parents at their house overnight without us also being on the island in case of an emergency. This felt strange but appropriate too, a little more intimate, ideal then, given that we were intending to "conceive" new life. We stayed in the same hotel we had stayed in for the initial treatment three years earlier, which also felt appropriate, ending the journey (or so we hoped) where it had begun.

The next morning, I was able to practice yoga on my own to help centre myself, before walking around the beautiful grounds of the hotel with E. Strangely, it was another clear, wintery morning, as it had been the previous time we had stayed, and again, I practiced some yoga in the deer circle before hugging the very old cedar tree and saying my prayers to the ethereal beings.

At the clinic, it was far less clinical than it had been in October. The nurse was known to us and the consultant was friendly and personable, and this time, we got to see the star of the blastocyst going into my uterus on the screen – hoorah! When we left, we said goodbye to the consultant and the nurse, and I was fairly confident we wouldn't need to return to the clinic again.

I felt the energy of the blastocyst in my tummy immediately; it was strong and vibrant, expansive too, full of the potential of new life. I felt blessed again to have had the opportunity to connect to the energy of life from conception like this, and it gave me immense comfort during my pregnancy, but especially in those earlier days. I couldn't quite get my head around the fact that this blastocyst had been frozen for three years and yet, still contained such vibrant energy. Isn't science amazing?

However, even though I could feel this energy and had faith in a positive outcome, I was still challenged by the 12-day waiting period to take the test. I would sit at the beginning of my yoga practice and notice where I was feeling sensation in my body, and inevitably, it was in my stomach, and as I dropped my awareness deeper into it, I recognised it as fear and anxiety. So I sat with this uncomfortable sensation, curious to see what happened, and inevitably, there would be a shift and the anxiety would ease.

It was ridiculous really, because while there was the fear and anxiety, there was also this knowing that all would be well and the Universe was certainly leaving me plenty of signs to validate this. Three days before the test, someone at work made an offhand comment about me being the next lady in the office to get pregnant – ha-ha, if only they knew.

The next day, on a training course this time, we were given a pink USB stick that one of the guys mentioned looked like a pregnancy testing stick. He accidentally dropped it on the floor and it landed just by me, so he reached down to pick it up and said to me, "Oh, it says you're pregnant, Emma." I chuckled to myself because little did he know that in two days' time I would be taking a test that would hopefully tell me this!

There were other signs too – the child-related cards flew out of my pack of angel cards, and robins and feathers were everywhere I looked, so I knew I was surrounded by the angels. This is not to say that there's anything special about me, just that I had aligned myself on that level and was feeling the support of the Universe, which really helped to keep my spirit high.

It was 5a.m. on testing day when I took the test, this time handing it to E and me snuggling up with him and Elijah in bed. Fortunately, it validated what I already knew. I was pregnant! The Goddess of the Moon had bestowed me with another child and I was ecstatic. I couldn't stop smiling. E was relieved, and my parents were joyful. My dream was coming true. Maybe now I'd get the spiritual awakening that can accompany birth – a homebirth, or so I hoped.

Chapter 25

High Risk Pregnancy?

The morning sickness arrived earlier, at five weeks this time, and I felt awful. It was all-consuming and particularly challenging with a toddler in tow. There just wasn't the opportunity to rest, as there had been during my first pregnancy, and I struggled with this.

At seven weeks' gestation, I bled. I felt pretty certain that I was meant to have this baby, but this experience certainly tested my faith again. I could still feel the energy of the baby within me, and my pendulum was also suggesting that all was well, but the blood made me think otherwise.

It was a nervous hour as we waited to see the doctor, who confirmed that whilst my cervix was closed, there was still a high chance of miscarriage. She referred me on to our initial specialist, Mr Nzewi, who managed to see me the next day.

We were due a seven-week early pregnancy scan anyway, and it was a relief to see the heart beating on the screen; our growing embryo was alive and well, and my faith was strengthened. It was also a reminder that we are all heart. It's a profound moment when you get to see this, and I remind myself of this frequently; it's as if we were given the opportunity to see into the essence of life on this planet. It's absolutely all about heart and the sooner we all realise this, the better the chance for peace on Mother Earth.

However, I did have a clot in my uterus that was significantly larger than the growing embryo, so I was placed on bed rest for a week. This was a blessing of sorts, as it provided me with an opportunity to rest, and helped ease me through this stage of the sickness, as I was able to sleep and work on my creative project from the comfort of my bed!

After the week of bed rest, life returned to normal – well, as much as it can when you feel dreadfully sick – and over time, the clot was re-absorbed by my body. This whole episode reminded me of the need to take it more slowly, and this certainly impacted on my yoga practice.

As I mentioned earlier, when I was pregnant with Elijah, I continued with my active vinyasa practice, making little allowance for the pregnancy. Yet now, I felt very differently about the style of yoga and relished taking the practice gently. I adopted a much more feminine approach to my practice, still inspired greatly by the teachings of Uma Dinsmore-Tuli. I also made sure to incorporate Yoga Nidra, and resting when I could to support the pregnancy.

I still taught yoga throughout my pregnancy, although now, with a toddler to look after, I wasn't teaching as much as I was during my first pregnancy. I was no longer teaching private yoga, for example, and was only teaching one evening class a week and two morning classes. I'm not sure I would have coped with any more than this. I was also only offering ad hoc Reiki sessions now, more so due to time constraints rather than anything else, but this did mean that I wasn't spreading myself so thin.

The energy of this baby felt different than Elijah's energy had at this stage of the pregnancy, which I found fascinating. S/he was less active, which concerned me at times, and encouraged me to dig deep and trust that all would be well. S/he felt much more grounded though, and I had a sense that this was my healing baby.

Homebirth

I considered that perhaps this time, I would be able to homebirth, and even though E was a little uncertain, I engaged the services of my doula, Anita, again, who is incredibly supportive of homebirth. I wanted to have the spiritual birth experience that I hadn't been able to have with Elijah, and I wanted to do all I could to avoid having another caesarean section.

I was challenged, therefore, when the initial midwife scored me as being "high risk".

"High risk, what on earth for?" I demanded to know.

"Well, you're over 40 years old, you've had a previous caesarean section, and you've had IVF," the midwife explained.

"But that's ridiculous," I tried to explain, "I'm fit and healthy and keen to homebirth."

"Oh, you won't be able to do that," she told me. "You'll be under specialist care now."

And with that, the frustration began to set in again because there was nothing wrong with me (no placenta previa for a start!).

It didn't help that when I saw the specialist for my initial consultation, he was surprised I didn't want a repeat caesarean section. "Absolutely not," I tried to tell him. "I had a bad experience last time and I certainly don't want to repeat that again."

With that, he told me that my risk factors meant that there was absolutely no way that I could have a homebirth. I was also not going to be allowed to go beyond 40 weeks without intervention, and a caesarean section would likely become another reality.

I was incensed. The specialist was new to the island and seemed overly cautious, and I didn't feel that he was listening to me. E had accompanied me to the appointment, and whilst he was pleased to hear that a homebirth was not going to be an option, he too felt that me being deemed "high risk" was ridiculous.

There was another aspect to the appointment that also challenged me. I knew with certainty the date of conception, as the clinic had confirmed this to me, but the 12-week dating scan had given me an estimated due date three days earlier than the "real" one. While this doesn't sound like a big deal, I am very aware that the due date can play a significant role in one's experience of late pregnancy and birth. And now, with the specialist talking about not letting me go beyond 40 weeks, those three days of discrepancy in due date became increasingly important to me. I didn't want the computer-generated earlier due date, I wanted the due date given to me by the clinic, which was 2nd December, two days after E's 50th birthday.

At the second appointment, I got angry. The specialist was again talking about a caesarean section being the safest option for delivery, and I insisted that I absolutely did not want a caesarean section, nor did I want intervention at 40 weeks, which may inevitably lead to a caesarean section, and I absolutely didn't want continuous monitoring of the baby during labour either.

He tried to stress the fact to me that the health of the baby was the most important thing to consider in terms of delivery. I didn't disagree with him, but I did mention that my emotional and mental needs were important too, and with that I tried to explain how awful I had felt following Elijah's birth and how I didn't want to feel like that again.

He then asked me to tell him how I believed he should prioritise between the health and wellbeing of the baby and my mental and emotional needs, which incensed me further. Of course, he needed to consider the health and wellbeing of the baby – that went without saying – but asking me to prioritise this was ridiculous. In my eyes, it didn't have to be so black and white.

E was also tested by this specialist's approach to the birth of our baby. He appreciated my need for a vaginal birth and didn't understand why that was going to be so difficult to achieve. He challenged the specialist on this but the specialist wasn't listening.

I was high risk and that was that. This meant growth scans throughout my pregnancy and a clinical birth. By the end of the appointment, I felt disempowered, angry and frustrated. I didn't want a caesarean section and I didn't want the baby arriving earlier than it chose to arrive. Frankly, I didn't want any of this. I just wanted an empowering, joyful and spiritually-enlightening homebirth.

This whole episode offered me a huge insight into how easily manipulated women are during pregnancy and how easily you can drop into a place of fear. During my first pregnancy, I'd read extensively about birthing without fear, and yet, here I was again, full of fear. The specialist had tapped into my vulnerability and made me feel that my body was incapable of growing or birthing a baby without medical assistance.

I also felt that to choose an alternative birthing route would make me an incredibly irresponsible mother, putting my baby and my life at risk. It didn't help that E had also been affected by the fear, and so I had the pressure of that too. While I desperately wanted to tap into and trust my body wisdom, the pressure to get it "right" was now huge; trying for the birth of my choice seemed a massive undertaking.

I decided I couldn't see that specialist again. His approach to my pregnancy was detrimentally affecting my experience of the pregnancy and making me feel sad and vulnerable. I cancelled my next couple of appointments with him and yet, felt wayward even doing this – what if I did end up needing specialist care after all? I just wanted it all to go away and considered that my best option was birthing in a field on my own and seeing what happened!

My doula was aware of how disempowered I felt as a result of my specialist appointments and encouraged me to seek a resolution. As such, I ended up contacting the Consultant Midwife here in Guernsey, and explained to her my concerns about the specialist-led care and also the fact I was keen to birth at home if I could.

She was wonderful, a true angel. She listened to me, which is something the specialist didn't do, and this in itself was hugely empowering. She also took action and arranged for me to see another specialist who she felt would be more compassionate to, and understanding of, my needs. She also confirmed that the midwife team would support me in my quest for a homebirth.

I could have cried with the relief. All of a sudden, I felt liberated and supported, and with that, I felt that I could enjoy my pregnancy again.

After the morning sickness eased at 16 weeks, I really enjoyed this second pregnancy. I've written about it before, but morning sickness is so debilitating and it was a relief when it ended. Of course, it was tiring, especially as Elijah was still waking at least once a night and wanted to be carried all the time, but it was a highlight in my life; I felt truly blessed.

I continued reading extensively on vaginal birth after caesarean section (often called VBAC) and also on home birthing. I felt comfortable with my decision to try for a homebirth and decided that I would delay that conversation with my new specialist for as long as possible. In many respects, I should have opted not to see a specialist at all, but when you're in the system, it is very difficult to get yourself out of it without being made to feel irresponsible.

I finally saw the new specialist, a lovely lady who was much more appreciative of my need to try for a vaginal birth. However she, like the other specialist, was adamant that I shouldn't be considering a homebirth, regardless of the midwives' opinion on the matter. She stressed the risk factors of a VBAC at home, which was frustrating, because I felt fear rear its ugly head again and I had to be mindful of allowing the medical perspective to disempower me again.

I do laugh because it seems so remarkable that we have managed to populate the world as we have when birth is considered so dangerous. I appreciate there are risks. The initial specialist had been keen to highlight this to me, when he quoted birthing vaginally in Afghanistan as being a very different experience from birthing vaginally in Guernsey. Women and babies regularly die from childbirth in Afghanistan, yet they don't here, and we have the medical world to thank for that. And I guess we do really. But all the same...

There was still a high chance that, despite all my efforts for a homebirth, it was not going to happen because, rather annoyingly, at 29 weeks, my baby was laying breech. I had already noticed this. I had stupidly demonstrated a handstand in class the week earlier, and whether this had been the reason, I'll never know, but it certainly hadn't helped.

I was annoyed at myself for jeopardising the position of the baby. Elijah had been breech, but due to the placenta previa, it hadn't really mattered, so I had continued inverting during my yoga practice. But this time, I had been practicing yoga incredibly gently to ensure that this baby didn't end up breech too.

Needless to say, the specialist was keen to point out to me (as it was her job to do so) that if the baby remained breech at 36 weeks then we would need to discuss options for delivery. Sadly, breech babies are no longer allowed to be birthed vaginally and so a caesarean section would be the only option. Where was my luck?! I now had another hurdle to overcome, and with that, I took myself off to read all I could on breech babies and turning them around.

Chapter 26

Trying to Turn a Breech Baby

I had seven weeks to turn my breech baby before the specialist would start talking about the need for a caesarean section. It sounded like plenty of time.

I began reading extensively on breech birth and discovered that about 3% of babies present as breech, which was just typical really, and summed up my pregnancies. There was always something that had to be different about them!

Still, most babies who are in the breech position between 32 to 34 weeks turn themselves into a headfirst position by birth. If the baby remains breech at 37 weeks, it may be possible for an obstetrician to turn the baby using a technique called external cephalic version. This is where the obstetrician tries to turn the baby into the head-down position by applying pressure to the abdomen. While it's a safe procedure, it can be a bit uncomfortable for the mother, especially if the uterus starts contracting. It is said that just over half of babies are turned this way.

Doing what I could to turn my baby

There were other ways, and I was directed to www.spinningbabies.com, which has lots of information about breech babies and tips on how to turn them. I was determined to try everything I could.

Initially, I tried the breech tilt, which meant that I lay upside down on an ironing board that had one end resting up against the bed. I'd come across this concept a few years earlier, when I'd read a fictional book about a Canadian midwife employing such tactics to help a baby turn. It had stuck in my mind as an ingenious way to help prevent breech delivery and now, here I was, doing the same.

If I'm truthful, it wasn't the most comfortable position to put myself in, especially with a pregnancy bump. Also, I didn't know how I was going to find the time to lie in the specified upside-down, tilted position for 20 minutes, three times a day, every day, the recommended time period if you stand a chance of it working. Besides, what exactly was I going to do while lying there? It's certainly not the ideal position for meditating or Yoga Nidra.

I decided I'd be better off practicing more headstands and shoulder stands during my daily yoga practice instead. It was the same with the turning-baby-tip of doing handstands in a swimming pool; I decided I'd just practice more handstands against the wall at home instead. It was ironic really, as I still couldn't be sure that it wasn't the handstand that had gotten me into this mess in the first place, although I had this feeling it would have happened regardless.

Then there was the moxibustion, which uses tightly-rolled sticks of mugwort herb, much like a stick of incense. You light one end of the moxibustion stick and the coal that this creates is held over an acupuncture point on the foot to heat it and help the baby turn. E thought it was nonsense but I felt that it was worth a try.

So, while I lay on the sofa reading a book, E tried to hold the heated stick at the right place on my foot. I have to say that despite being very receptive to this sort of thing, I just wasn't feeling it. I mean literally, there wasn't any shift in the positioning of the baby, and furthermore, I couldn't be sure that E was positioning the stick properly.

I also tried reflexology, cranial-sacral work and Bowen therapy. I am a huge fan of homeopathy, so I tapped into this too, and took the homeopathic remedy Pulsatilla. I had read that if taking this remedy for three days does not turn the baby then it is unlikely the baby will turn. Unfortunately, after three days, the baby had not turned.

It was then that I came across this marvellous blog post detailing the authoress' journey to try to turn her breech baby (unfortunately, I didn't keep a note of her website to be able to share with you, but if you're meant to find it then you will; there's a whole heap out there to look through). This lady wrote about how she'd tried all the same techniques that I had tried and that nothing had worked. Then, at the last minute, she'd had a massive emotional meltdown and totally let go… and lo and behold, right at the last minute, the baby turned.

I really didn't want to have any medical intervention, so this blog post gave me some hope. I was getting pretty desperate by this stage and was determined that something had to work; the baby had to turn. It was probably in recognising my desperation, and being so frustrated that nothing was working, that I too had a big emotional meltdown, the tears flooding my yoga mat one morning.

The baby didn't turn, but there was still hope. I was told stories of pregnant ladies being prepped to go to theatre for a caesarean section, only for the midwife to double-check the baby's position, and find that at the last moment, the baby had flipped head down and could be birthed vaginally.

The trouble was, I had this niggling feeling that this baby just wasn't going to turn. It seemed very comfortable in its breech position and no amount of manipulation on my part seemed to make any difference. Furthermore, no amount of shoulder stands, headstands or handstands had any effect either. And with the other techniques, well, I was just going through the motions really, as E looked on, bemused!

I continued my research and discovered that there are a number of physical reasons that one may have a breech baby, including the following:

- Smaller than average baby;
- In multiple pregnancies, one baby may be lying in the breech position;
- There may not be enough, or too much, amniotic fluid;
- The placenta may be covering the womb's entrance (like I had with Elijah);

- Tightness in the womb or pelvic misalignment, perhaps from carrying a toddler on one's hip.

I could relate to some of this. I had started to see a biodynamic cranial sacral therapist, as I was having issues with my sacrum and felt that my pelvis was misaligned, due to constantly carrying Elijah on my left hip. However, I also had a feeling that there was more to it than all this, and so I researched the non-physical reasons for a breech presentation too. These included the following:

- The mother-to-be harbouring a lot of fear about becoming a mother;
- The mother-to-be and her mother having unresolved conflict;
- The mother-to-be not wanting to "give up" carrying her baby;
- The mother needing to "hold" the baby close to her heart due to fears of birth, parenthood, and/or fear about the world the baby will be born into.

In a similar vein, others believe that the baby can sense when their mothers are stressed or in emotional pain, and may move into a breech position so that they can be closer to her heart in order to comfort her – a breech baby may have strong instincts already.

There's also a belief that breech babies are on a mission in this lifetime and arrive feet first so that they can firmly plant their feet on the Earth and get going. Others believe they arrive this way so that they can look their mother in the eye and move through life together, and yet, with a strong conviction of their own. Folklore suggests that breech babies have healing powers.

I found this all very fascinating, as I could relate to some of it. My life was busy and there were times where I was stressed. I was working very hard on a few projects that I was keen to complete before the baby arrived. In my mind,

I had given myself the deadline of my October Herm Yoga and Wellbeing Retreat, when I would be 33 weeks pregnant, to complete everything. After that, I intended to slow things down up until the anticipated birth at 40 weeks. I thought I had allowed seven calm weeks to prepare myself.

However, sitting with it during my daily meditation practice, and trying to really feel into it, into my body, I began to consider that perhaps this wasn't about me, that perhaps it was part of the bigger picture. This is not to say that I didn't still feel a pressure to turn the baby, but more so that I had a feeling the baby was not going to turn, regardless of what I did. Thus, I started to read up on breech delivery and was fascinated by what I read.

Beginning in the 1960s, obstetricians gradually shifted the way they delivered breech babies because they preferred the predictability and the presumed greater safety of a caesarean birth. But not every doctor jumped on the caesarean section bandwagon immediately, with many continuing to favour vaginal breech births instead.

That is, until the Hannah Term Breech Trial ("TBT"), published in 2000, brought them to a screeching halt. The TBT followed 2,088 breech babies at 121 centres in 26 countries, randomly assigned to either vaginal or planned caesarean section birth. Early data suggested fewer new-born deaths and injuries occurred in the caesarean section group. The impact of the study was incredible – within months, breech caesarean sections increased from 50% to 80%, and by 2006, it was at 90%. Then it was discovered that the study was flawed.

In fact, critics began poking holes in the TBT immediately after its publication. For example, some poor outcomes attributed to vaginal delivery occurred in birth centres that used substandard techniques or unskilled birth attendants. Some babies had genetic defects or were premature.

In short, most weren't injured because they were delivered vaginally, but because of other factors. Further studies indicated that most of the babies recovered fully from their birth injuries, regardless of delivery method, and researchers had also not factored in the increased health risks resulting from caesarean sections.

The results should have supported informed decision-making, but instead, hospitals reacted by taking the choice away from women. Another unfortunate result was that medical schools stopped teaching vaginal breech delivery skills to an entire generation of new doctors and midwives. This, sadly, is the current reality we face – that the medical profession lack both the knowledge and skill to deliver a breech baby vaginally.

I watched a number of videos on the Internet of breech babies being born vaginally and there was something special and beautiful about these births. My doula shared my sentiments and also feels that it is a shame that breech vaginal delivery is not supported by the medical profession these days. Sadly, we're in the minority, for when I mentioned to people generally that I would like to have a go at a vaginal breech delivery, I was surprised by their reaction – there was so much fear!

I was told that the birth would be extremely painful, and that I would be putting my baby's health at risk. I was made to feel that I was silly for even suggesting the idea – and this wasn't just the medical profession, but friends and family too. It made me laugh because the alternative, a caesarean section, is not exactly a walk in the park either – it's just easier for the medical profession to control.

I spoke to the Consultant Midwife about the possibility of a vaginal breech delivery, and she said that even if a specialist agreed to this, it wouldn't be a birth I would want for my baby (or for me), due to the medicalised nature of it, with constant monitoring and doubtlessly intervention, whether it was needed or not.

This makes me feel sad even now that there is so much fear surrounding breech vaginal birth, and how this becomes such a downer for so many women during their pregnancy. My cousin was a breech baby and born vaginally, and my aunt lives to tell the tale. And clearly, breech babies continue to be born vaginally, certainly in the home environment, with the support of those independent midwives who have maintained the skills necessary to support a breech delivery. I was heartened to read that there are murmurs of trying to normalise breech vaginal birth again.

This gave me a little hope, and I certainly wasn't prepared to give up on the idea. I played around with the possibility of employing the skills of an independent midwife in the UK, but something held me back from taking this forward. I was very much of the mindset that I would just wait and see what happened nearer the time, as I had a feeling that it would all become clearer. Ha, little could I have imagined…

Chapter 27

Did My Waters Just Break or Did I Wet Myself?

In my infinite wisdom, I decided to run a Yoga and Wellbeing Retreat in the October that I would be 33 weeks pregnant. I didn't foresee any issues, as I'd taught yoga until 36 weeks during my first pregnancy, and whilst Elijah had been born at 38.5 weeks' gestation, that was due to a planned caesarean section for placenta previa. I'd decided that once the retreat had finished, I would take life more slowly and gently. I should've known better – life has a habit of not always turning out as you intend, especially when you invite the Goddess of the Moon into it.

Ordinarily, I am helped on retreat by one of my friend's, Vicki, who is also a qualified yoga teacher. She is an amazing yoga adjustor and a complement to the classes. However, she had initially planned to be on holiday at the time of the retreat, so I commandeered the services of another local qualified yoga teacher, Jade, instead.

Nearer to the time, Vicki's plans changed, and initially, I was fairly adamant that I didn't need her help in addition to Jade. However, the weekend prior to the retreat, I contracted a tummy bug that made me feel rotten. I spent a day in bed feeling very sorry for myself and had to ask Vicki to cover my evening yoga class for me.

It was then, lying in bed on that Monday, with the retreat due to start on the Friday, that I had this sense that I needed Vicki to help me on the retreat too. Fortunately, she was keen to do so, and with that, I felt a sense of relief. Whilst I had no reason to doubt my ability to teach on the retreat, I was tired, as I had been busy building up to it and I welcomed the extra moral support as much as anything else.

An Aries super full moon was due to peak at 4.23a.m. on the Sunday, the retreat finishing later that morning at 11a.m. I love full moons and this super full moon was meant to be all about ramming through fear, changing what you can change, and surrendering to the rest. It was ideal material for the retreat and provided our focus… face the fear and surrender to it… I was especially focused on inviting the students to really tap into their fears and see if they could surrender to these during the weekend. I'm sure I bored them senseless going on about it!

On the Friday afternoon, prior to the guests arriving, I did my own practice in the beautiful yoga space and felt something shift in my pelvis. The sensation sent me into minor panic because something didn't feel right, but I didn't have too much time to reflect on it, as the participants were shortly due to arrive. Still, I spent that evening a little on edge, desperate to feel the baby kicking. It seemed he/she was having a quiet one, chilling out in my womb instead.

On the Saturday, I joined the others for the usual early morning swim in the sea and was heartened that I could feel the baby kicking as usual. I was very aware of the full moon energy building, and I continued to stress this to everyone during the day.

That early afternoon, I did another practice on my own, a womb-based one this time, using some of the sequences detailed in Uma Dinsmore-Tuli's book, *Yoni Shakti* (an incredible book if you're a fan of yoga for women, at all stages of life), ahead of the womb-based class I was intending to teach that afternoon, and I felt something shift again. I wasn't quite sure what it was, but later that afternoon, when I went for a walk with Vicki, I felt as if the baby had dropped, and I found myself holding the base of my bump, as if to keep it up and hold the baby in. It was a strange feeling.

After dinner that evening, I played with Elijah, lifting him up and rolling on the ground with him, having lots of fun together, before bedtime. On the way to our room, I bought myself a strawberry quartz bracelet that Athene, one of my jeweller friends, was selling on an honesty-box basis for the retreat participants. It had been catching my eye all day and I decided that now was the time to wear it.

Little did I realise how quickly the energy of this bracelet would get to work. Apparently, the energy of strawberry quartz supports your emotional body, helping to heal and release negative emotional patterns that don't serve you, bringing your emotions into harmony so that you live your life with an appreciation for, and gratitude to, all that life brings.

Back in the hotel room and with Elijah asleep, I ordered the book *The Universe Has Your Back* by Gabrielle Bernstein from Amazon, which I'd seen pop up when I'd been looking for another book online, days earlier. I had seven weeks until my due date and I wanted the Universe to have my back – or help me turn my breech baby. Either that or I was going to have to face my fear of having another caesarean section, and learn how to surrender to it.

My waters

After reading, I went to sleep at about 10p.m. while E was still with friends, merrily drinking their way through a bottle or two of wine in the Mermaid pub on Herm. About 11p.m., I awoke, feeling something wet in the bed, which was unusual and felt very strange. I quickly realised the source of the wetness was coming from me! E was in bed by then, and I tried not to wake him as I rushed to the toilet.

I initially considered that I'd just wet myself, then I realised that the water was continuing to flow out of me. I had never experienced waters breaking previously, due to the planned caesarean section with Elijah, so it was all new to me. I woke E and explained what I thought was going on. He didn't really know what to make of it, so I sent a quick text to Anita, hoping that she was still awake and would be able to help me.

Fortunately, she saw the message on her way to bed and quickly responded. She also asked whether perhaps I'd wet myself, but when I explained that I still had water coming out of me, she agreed, it seemed my waters had broken.

This was not ideal timing, and for a split second, I considered that we might just have to see what happened in the morning, as I had a yoga retreat to finish – there was still another class to teach in the morning.

However, Anita telephoned and told me in no uncertain terms that I needed to phone the hospital, that probably a lifeboat would be sent to collect E and I. It all sounded a bit dramatic, I didn't want all this fuss for no reason, but I also couldn't deny the fact that my waters had broken – early, and with me carrying a breech baby!

E telephoned the maternity ward at the hospital in Guernsey and the midwife told us to come into the ward, but of course, we couldn't do that, we were stuck on Herm, three miles away from the east coast of Guernsey! So there began a rather challenging few hours as arrangements were made to "rescue" us and transport us to the hospital on Guernsey.

Fortunately, my parents were also staying with us on Herm, and amazingly, they answered their mobile phone and joined us in our room within five minutes of calling. By then, I was shaking uncontrollably, not least because of the fear of the unknown, but also because of all the fuss that was being made just for me. Strange though it may sound, it was almost a relief to continuously leak water, as if to confirm that yes, I really did need to go to the hospital.

GETTING RESCUED

There was a lot of to-ing and fro-ing with various telephone conversations between E, the paramedics and the midwives, and we were told to wait until the Herm first aider came to collect us. This seemed to take quite some time, over an hour or so, and the waiting was a very "present-moment" experience as I was in hyper alert mode.

On the positive side, we had time to make arrangements for the rest of the retreat. My parents would now need to stay in our room with Elijah, and Vicki would need to teach the class in the morning and close the retreat. I'd already made notes detailing what I'd wanted to say to bring the retreat to a close, and I now wrote a message to Vicki explaining this, and thanking her for covering for me!

Eventually, Mark, the first aider, arrived on his John Deere Gator and drove us the short distance to Rosaire Steps, where we were due to meet the lifeboat. Ordinarily, the "Flying Christine", the St John Ambulance boat, would have collected me, but it was deemed too rough for it to launch that evening. E was sitting beside me on the Gator and I remember commenting to him that Elijah would have loved to be with us, as he loves Gators!

The full moon was due to peak in an hour or so and the tide was extremely low. It was also blowing a gale and the lifeboat was having trouble mooring. It didn't help that this was a loaned lifeboat; the usual one was out of service at the time.

Thus, we spent an hour or so standing on the quay chatting, as we watched the lifeboat crew try to figure out how to reach us. It was ironic really; I had spotted the lifeboat on the quay alongside the Herm boat when we left Guernsey on the Friday morning, which was unusual because it's not something I normally noticed. And now, here I was, watching it trying to rescue me – it was clearly a sign!

What was particularly amusing, however, was the fact that the super moon was full above us. There she was, the Goddess of the Moon, in all her glory, shining brightly, her light reflected on the sea. I had to laugh because, of course, I'd been going on and on all weekend about the power of the super full moon, and here I was now, standing beneath her light as she reached her peak in the early hours of that Sunday morning. I'll never forget that image of her that night.

The outboard motor of the inshore dinghy wouldn't work, which meant that the lifeboat crew couldn't come out to collect us in the dinghy. I was fairly calm about the whole situation, distracted a little because the lifeboat crew were having such a hard time trying to get to us and heartened that there was the moon shining overhead. Mark kept chatting with us and making us laugh, keeping our spirits high.

Furthermore, I felt this incredible sense that the Universe had our back, to the extent that I was almost smiling to myself about the unfolding of events with the moon shining above. I couldn't make it up better if I tried. There I was, my waters breaking during the Herm Yoga and Wellbeing retreat I was leading, and there was the lifeboat crew unable to reach us, so we were standing there for a good hour or so. In fact, my dad came to check on us as he and my mum had been waiting to see the lifeboat head back to Guernsey and they'd grown concerned that there had been a complication with the waters breaking.

Anita was on tenterhooks in Guernsey too, desperate to know what was going on and whether she needed to come and meet us in the hospital. E and I just saw it for what it was; we didn't know what was happening and were contended to let it unfold, knowing that we were in safe hands. Admittedly, it was a rough night at sea, but we were only three miles from Guernsey, and while I had water leaking out of me, I wasn't in pain and didn't have any contractions.

Eventually, anchored by lines, E and I were transferred shore to ship in a little rowing boat (how we laugh about this now) and helped to climb up onto the lifeboat. On board was a midwife and two female paramedics, who'd had a tough hour or so bobbing around on board. This was my first time in a lifeboat and I couldn't quite comprehend all this fuss was just for me, and I was almost a little embarrassed because it wasn't like I was in labour.

The tide was so extremely low that the lifeboat had to go the long way back to Guernsey, and there was a significant swell, which meant that the boat was moving about dramatically at times. The midwife was keen to get me back to Guernsey as quickly as possible and the crew did their best to facilitate this.

I was seated in the padded and sprung chair, which was a relief, as it absorbed much of the shock that the others had to endure. I'll never forget that journey though, as it did nothing to ease my nerves. The lifeboat was tossed around and I felt decidedly sick by the end of the trip. Poor E wasn't in a sprung chair and his stomach didn't like the ride either, his back was also sore from the experience.

Back on dry land on Guernsey, we were met by an ambulance and driven to the hospital. It was surreal being on the road in the early hours of the morning as party revellers returned home. I felt a bit of a fraud in an ambulance, as I felt fine, other than the fact I had water dripping out of my vagina, wetting my pants and leggings.

Too Soon

At the hospital, my lovely lady specialist happened to be on duty, which was fortunate as we were able to joke about the manner in which my pregnancy was unfolding. She knew I was keen for a vaginal birth, and that the baby had turned breech and would need to turn to facilitate this. And now, here I was, at 33 weeks, with my waters broken. It wasn't ideal.

An internal examination confirmed that my waters had indeed broken, but that I was not yet in labour. According to my midwifery records, my due date, based on the dating scan, showed that I was 33 weeks and 6 days pregnant. This meant that the baby was – in theory at least – only a day away from having fully developed lungs. The specialist was keen, therefore, that we did all we could to promote the development of his/her lungs and and keep him/her in utero until at least 34 weeks' gestation, so one more day.

It was agreed that I would remain in hospital for the initial 24 hours so that I could be monitored for infection and be administered steroids to help the baby's lungs fully develop. Furthermore, if I was going to go into early labour, then it was more likely to happen in that 24-hour period following the waters breaking.

Thus, I was immediately prescribed steroids, which would be administered to me over the following 24-hour period, while I was kept on the ward for observation. I remember the specialist and nurse leaving E and I in the triage room to go and make the necessary arrangements and me bursting into tears and clinging on to him.

I wasn't ready to have the baby. I'd had it in my mind all pregnancy that I would work hard until my Herm retreat and then calm it down a bit. I had been looking forward to the calmer period, focusing on my pregnancy and trying to turn the baby, and now, here I was with my waters broken. I wasn't prepared, mentally or emotionally.

Furthermore, I wasn't at all prepared practically. All the baby stuff was in storage and I hadn't gotten around to sorting it yet. Clothes needed to be washed and the Moses basket found. I hadn't bought any nappies or other stuff required for a small baby, and I certainly hadn't packed my hospital bag.

However, whether I was ready or not, this was really happening, and half an hour later, I found myself trying to get comfortable in a hospital bed on the maternity ward, while E walked the short distance home. It was all a little surreal and I sobbed quietly to myself as I tried to get some sleep, all the while, my mind trying to come to terms with what was happening.

Chapter 28

Preterm Pre-Labour Rupture of the Membranes

One of the few things I had brought with me to the hospital from Herm was my laptop, so after a few hours of restless sleep, I gave up trying and researched all I could on "waters breaking early" instead.

PPROM

The baby lies in an amniotic sac of fluid or "waters", and "waters breaking" means that the sac has ruptured. My body was continuously replacing amniotic fluid to protect the baby, but as the sac was broken, it was not retained and was constantly trickling out of me. It was the strangest sensation and I had to wear pads to collect the fluid, and these needed to be changed regularly. The fluid was a clear/pinkish colour and I had to keep checking that this didn't become greenish or brown, which would indicate infection. I was encouraged to drink lots of water to enable the body to use this to create the amniotic fluid.

Waters normally break around the time that labour is due, but in around 2% of pregnancies, they break early – where was my luck again? The medical term for this condition is PPROM, which stands for Preterm Pre-labour Rupture of the Membranes, and means that the waters have broken before the baby has reached full term (37 weeks).

Statistics suggest that intrauterine infection is responsible for around one third of women with PPROM, but the reason for the other two thirds is largely unknown, although it has been linked to heavy smoking during pregnancy. At that time, I didn't have any signs of infection and I wasn't a smoker, so it was considered just "one of those things". I couldn't help thinking however, that the Goddess of the Moon had a role to play in all this and certainly that role became clearer in the days ahead.

Like most, I had thought that once the waters break, the pregnant lady immediately goes into labour – this is certainly what most of my students, friends and family thought, as everyone assumed I must have had the baby. However, I discovered that this isn't the case, contrary to the scene depicted in many a film, such as *Bridget Jones's Baby*, which is a classic example of this.

When waters break early, the treatment is dependent on the stage of the pregnancy. There is an increased risk of going into labour prematurely and this brings with it the health risks for the baby of early birth, which are obviously greater the younger they are. On the other hand, if the woman doesn't go into labour, there is a risk of infection for both mother and baby.

The specialists had to balance these two considerations. If the waters had broken because of infection, then there would be an increased risk of the baby getting the infection and delivery may have to be immediate.

When the waters have broken but there is no infection present, as in my case, then while both of us were still at risk, the immediate risk is lesser and the treatment depends again on the stage of pregnancy.

MONDAY

I found it funny – the Goddess of the Moon was up to her tricks again. Earlier on in the pregnancy, I had made a real fuss about the due date, as the dating scan at 12 weeks had given me an earlier date than the clinic. I couldn't understand the reason the medical profession would work from the computer-generated date, when I quite clearly knew the exact date of conception because of the clinical manner in which the baby had been conceived.

I was concerned, back then, of intervention at 40 weeks, as the specialist I initially saw told me that he wouldn't want me carrying the baby beyond the 40-week period. Thus, I had been very keen that the medical profession use the date given to me by the clinic, as this would "buy" me an extra four days of pregnancy before any talk of intervention.

Now, however, the earlier due date was working in my favour because it meant that I reached the "safe" 34 weeks four days earlier than if we had used the due date given to me by the clinic. Thus, when Monday (the next morning) arrived, I'd reached 34 weeks per the dating scan, and I was administered the final steroid. I could almost hear the midwives sigh with relief that we'd managed to get to that date without me going into labour.

Over the course of that initial twenty-four-hour period in hospital, I saw three different specialists and they all agreed that I should be allowed to go home and continue life as normal, except no baths, no sex and no teaching yoga. I was to return to the ward every other day for monitoring and to check for any signs of infection by continuing to regularly take my temperature and check my discharge, which was constantly trickling out of me.

The intention was to keep the baby in utero for as long as possible, but no longer than 37 weeks, when the baby is considered full term. At that point, I would need to have a caesarean section, as the baby was breech, and without the amniotic fluid, there was no way it could turn now. This was far from ideal, as I was still adamant that I didn't want to have a caesarean section, and I was going to do all I could to fight for a vaginal birth.

I raised the issue with each of the specialists in turn. My lovely lady specialist was adamant that it was not going to be an option. Another one was aware that the Hannah Term Breech Trial had been flawed, and that whilst there were risks with a breech delivery, there were also risks associated with a caesarean section, and it was a case of seeing what happened. The other wouldn't give an opinion either way and left me with some hope that possibly, I could convince him of a vaginal breech birth when we got to decision day.

I spoke to the midwives at length about breech birth too and enquired whether any of them would be able to facilitate this delivery, but the answer was a resounding "no". This is unsurprising, as I had already learned how much fear there is surrounding vaginal breech birth and that most midwives are not trained to support such a birth.

It was frustrating and yet, I was still so determined. I prayed with increased vigour for a resolution that would find the baby miraculously turning and tried to keep my thinking positive.

Around this time, I emailed my four close university friends and shared with them the recent events and my desperation to avoid another caesarean section. One of them had a planned caesarean section, as her son was also breech, and another had experienced both an emergency and a planned caesarean section. Both were keen to allay my fears and assure me that a caesarean birth could be empowering, intimate and beautiful.

While I was still stubbornly resistant to the idea of a repeat caesarean section, their comments did get me thinking. I knew, without doubt, that my experience of caesarean section had not been empowering, intimate or beautiful, yet, I began questioning whether that was due to the placenta previa more than the procedure per se.

I returned home from the hospital later that morning to find the book I had ordered on the Saturday, *The Universe Has Your Back* by Gabrielle Bernstein, had arrived. This book is about relinquishing the need to control our lives, to transmute fear into love, find safety in the face of uncertainty, joy in what might otherwise be pain, and to recognise that the Universe has your back. Its arrival in my life was certainly well timed.

If there was one thing I needed reminding of in that moment was that the Universe had my back and that there was a greater plan at work here. Deep down, I already knew this, but I realised that I needed to try to come to terms with the possibility of a caesarean section and address all the fears that were attached to this. I had to see the love, and strengthen my faith in a peaceful outcome, whatever that may mean.

Tuesday

My colleagues thought I was mad returning to work on the Tuesday morning with my waters broken, but the specialists believed that this was the safest option for me, as it meant I would be sitting for most of the day. They were all nervous though and there were jokes of a birth in the office and the need for hot water and towels – little did they realise the implication of the breech positioning of the baby at that time.

I felt fine, albeit that I was constantly leaking amniotic fluid and I couldn't feel the baby kicking so easily now, so there were moments of minor panic. However, the more I read my new book, the more I started to realise that this was all a lesson in overcoming fear and stepping into a place of love and trust instead.

I felt this overwhelming need to try to get on top of my workload and tie up loose ends. This feeling increased that evening and I had a fretful night's sleep, as my mind ran over and over all that I needed to do to ensure that my workload was in a position to hand over to someone else.

Wednesday

I awoke feeling energised and raring to get on with the day. Firstly, however, I felt an overwhelming need to get into the sea to cleanse and ground me. So E, Elijah and I all drove down to the beach together and I remember the intimacy of it, us a family of three, doing what we do best – going to the beach! While we were there, I mentioned this to E as I just had this feeling that this would be the last time the three of us would come to the beach like this together and I wanted to capture the moment.

After our invigorating swim and a warming shower back at home, I had to return to the hospital so that my temperature could be checked and the baby's heart could be monitored. Basically, this means that two flat devices (sensors) are held in place over the baby bump by elastic belts and the baby's heartbeat is recorded on a chart and checked for any abnormalities.

While lying there you also have to press a button each time the baby kicks so that the midwives can monitor the baby's movements. Other than that, I got to lie back and read my book, which was constantly reminding me to turn to love and away from fear.

Everything seemed fine. I didn't have a temperature and the baby's heartbeat was regular. I spoke to my lovely lady specialist and double-checked that it was still OK to be going into the office and working. I explained the reaction from my colleagues, but she assured me this was fine, however, she stressed that she didn't want me teaching any more yoga! Fortunately, Vicki was able to cover my classes for me.

From the hospital, I went into the office and my colleagues expressed concern again, surprised that I hadn't been signed off from work. I tried my best to allay their fears because, to be honest, I felt fine; the only slight irritant was the trickling of the amniotic fluid, which was making my nether regions sore.

I worked as quickly as I could to tie off the loose ends. I remember being so focused and busy that I didn't even stop to eat anything. I had resigned from my job a few months earlier, but a replacement had not yet been found, so I wrote notes detailing all aspects of my role so that someone could easily come in and pick this up from me if necessary.

It felt strange thinking that I wouldn't be continuing with the role after having the baby. It wasn't that I didn't like the job, I did, just that I didn't want to be constrained to a maternity leave dictated by company policy. I wanted to take as long as I needed at home with the baby this time, without having to return to work by a certain time period.

Admittedly, in that April, the Maternity Leave and Adoption Leave (Guernsey) Ordinance, 2016 had come into force that finally gave statutory rights to pregnant employees whose due date was after 7th August 2016. This applied to me, and meant that I was entitled to an enhanced maternity period of 26 weeks leave, as I had worked continuously for a period of 15 months for the same employer (otherwise, you only get a basic leave of 12 weeks).

This new statutory right was a blessing really, as my employer was forced to adhere to it. With Elijah, no such right had been available, and I was only able to take the basic leave of 12 weeks, per my company's policy at that time. This had not been long enough and it was utterly exhausting returning to work with a 12-week old who was still waking regularly at night and relying on me for his primary source of nourishment through my milk.

If anything, it felt cruel leaving Elijah at that age, and I was determined I wasn't going to do the same again, especially as E and I had both agreed that this would be our last baby. I wanted to enjoy every moment of his/her first six months or so in this world, and while I could have done that and retained my job with this new policy in place, I still didn't want the pressure of the job hanging over me. I didn't want to have to check my emails, or have people contact me about work, or feel any pressure to return earlier, if they weren't able to find someone to replace me.

Of course, there was the financial side to consider, but we felt that in the grand scheme of things, this was OK. We would try to keep our costs as low as possible. I would receive a maternity grant from the States of Guernsey, which would help, and we agreed to live off savings if necessary. It helped that I had every intention of teaching yoga during the maternity period as I don't really consider this working, but I wasn't going to rush back to this either.

I had plans that when I did feel ready to return to the workplace, I would take the bold step of working solely for myself as a freelance company secretary. I wanted the extra freedom that this would provide, and the opportunity to work from home when necessary. Plus, I was still involved in a few creative projects and I wanted the time and space to take these seriously.

I don't think anyone in the office really thought I was leaving for good. I was one of the initial employees and had helped to set up the company. Also, I'd already left once to go travelling around the world, and then found my way back into the office again when my replacement had gone off on maternity leave. Needless to say they hadn't given too much thought to a replacement for me; like me, they thought I still had an additional seven weeks to go until the arrival of the baby, so they were grateful for my notes on what to do if I wasn't in the office!

By 5p.m., I was finished, and it was a huge weight off my mind and shoulders. I felt like I could finally relax, although I had this overwhelming sense that I needed to go to a church and pray first. I collected E and Elijah from home and together, we drove the short distance to our local church, St Andrews, where E's dad's ashes are kept, but this was strangely closed. We visited E's dad's grave nonetheless, which felt appropriate, given the circumstances.

We then headed to St Martin's Church, as it was the next one closest to our home, and it was only when we arrived that I realised why we had been directed here. Outside the church is a granite standing stone or statue-menhir, which was carved into a female form some 4,000 years ago and is said to represent an earth goddess or earth mother figure, and is known as La Gran'mère du Chimquière, meaning the grandmother.

She has been an object of awe and reverence and is looked upon as a holy stone – the carvings are of a typical female figure, an earth mother form that depicts a Pagan fertility goddess, which strangely guards and protects a Christian church. New brides place flowers on her head for luck, and she is adorned with flowers on May Day.

I couldn't help feeling that I needed the energy and wisdom of this grandmother in my life now too, so I touched her, said a prayer, gave thanks and asked for her support. We then briefly visited the church and I prayed to Mother Mary for a miracle. I still wanted the baby to turn from its breech position and I was hoping for Divine intervention!

Comforted by our church visitation and seeing the grandmother – and marvelling at the manner in which we found ourselves face to face with her, yet another sign that all was well and the Universe was looking out for us – I returned home, feeling that now, I could allow myself to relax as everything was completed. It was perfect timing therefore for a facial appointment I had booked later that evening as a post-Herm retreat treat, an opportunity to finally relax, or so I thought!

Chapter 29

Dancing with the Moon

I started contracting during the facial treatment. I didn't realise what was happening at the time, I just thought it was some cramping. The sensation increased during the evening to the point that I found it difficult to sleep and it was then it dawned on me that the sensations were contractions.

I was jubilant; I was finally contracting! I had longed to experience this feeling, ever since it was denied to me with the planned delivery of Elijah, three years earlier. This time around, I had wanted the baby to choose its birthing date, and here it was, making that choice.

I loved every moment of that evening; it was one of the most intimate, magical and special experiences of my life. I shall always treasure the insight it provided, of my breath, of sensation, and of the opportunity to be joyfully present. Pain brings this gift to us, and there I was, able to rejoice with it.

Thursday

I spent some time on the sofa, dipping in and out of Facebook, aware of the time changing because the new day brought with it new birthdays. I shall never forget that, because I felt so pleased with myself, being one of the first people to congratulate a friend on her birthday.

When I had tired of that and the sensation demanded otherwise, I wrapped myself in a blanket and spent time outside in the darkness of the night, with the waning moon and the stars above me.

I squatted on the earth where Elijah's tree grows, with his placenta nourishing it, and where I'd bled prior to conceiving this new life growing inside me, and felt an incredible oneness with everything. It felt poignant, as if I was stepping into a portal that connected me to the mysteries of this world.

And then, the moment came, as I always hoped it would, when all I wanted to do was sway my hips and dance.

I danced with the moon, shining her light over me, as I held my baby within me. Together, we danced around the garden and I couldn't stop smiling because I was on my own and I was having the most amazing time.

I felt overwhelming love for my baby, and for Elijah and E, asleep inside, and for the world, and this oneness that goes as quickly as it comes. I felt truly aligned.

I danced with the moon until I knew it was time to go inside again.

There I lay, in the bath, cleansed by the water, focusing on breath and sensation, and on and on it went. I wasn't meant to be bathing, but the moment demanded otherwise; bathing was all I wanted to do to ease the sensations and relax in the warmth of the water, it's what I knew ladies did when they needed relief from contractions, and now I too was contracting! It was essential I bathed!

At some point during the early hours, I released my mucous plug, and whilst I was aware that if I was in labour, I was meant to telephone the ward immediately, I felt that I didn't need to do that just yet.

All fear had finally gone and there was this sense that perhaps I could just wing it. Perhaps I could just stay at home like this and see what happened, see whether I could birth my breech baby all on my own. I still hadn't given up on that hope. But I was aware that if it was meant to be, it would be, and that the baby would arrive quickly.

However, by 5.30a.m., there was no baby, and I began to realise that I had to do something about my situation. E was awake by then and I noticed that the discharge had started to change colour. It wasn't a clear/pinkish colour anymore, so I knew it was now time to telephone the hospital.

With E awake, the sensations felt stronger because I wasn't able to be in my space with my breath in the same way as I had been on my own. This was an insight to me, the potential need to be alone during the birthing experience.

DANCING WITH THE MOON

Not that I had that opportunity, because having telephoned the ward, they told me to come in immediately.

With Elijah now awake too, the three of us stepped out of the house into the darkness of the early morning, and there, up in the sky ahead of us, was the waning moon and the sign of a cross in the sky, made from two airline streams. It felt incredibly auspicious and I knew in my heart of hearts that now was the time, this was a sign, this was really happening.

We dropped Elijah off at E's mum's and went to the hospital, where I discovered that it's rather tricky to walk when you're contracting at the same time!

It's also rather tricky to lie still and be scanned. But alas, that is what happened, and it showed I was contracting, and a decision would soon need to be made about delivery because the specialists didn't want me going into full blown labour and running the risk of birthing a breech baby.

A swab was taken to test for an infection and I was allocated a bed on the ward. The specialist (coincidentally, the South African one who had delivered Elijah) felt that, one way or another, there was a high chance that the baby would be delivered that day. If the tests showed that I had an infection then the baby needed to be delivered that morning. If I didn't have an infection, there was a chance that now it was light outside, the contractions would stop and I would be monitored – the longer the baby was in utero, be better for his/her development (apparently contractions can be affected by the light).

I was *still* talking about breech birth because there was still hope. There was still a chance that the contractions would ease and I would have time.

I was aware that the extra-cautious specialist I had initially seen when I was first pregnant was also working the ward that morning and I was adamant that I didn't want to see him. He had told me I would be high risk and would likely deliver by caesarean section and here I was, about to do exactly that.

It didn't seem to matter anymore. By then, I'd finished reading *The Universe Has Your Back* and my mantra was "love not fear". And here I was, in hospital, very aware that yes, the Universe had my back, and what was meant to be was meant to be.

I had to surrender.

And then came the opportunity.

My lovely female specialist was now on duty and she came to see me with the South African specialist who we'd seen upon our arrival to the ward. They told us that the swab had been tested and showed that I had an infection.

She took my hand and told me that she knew this wasn't what I wanted to hear, but that there really was no choice now, the baby had to be delivered that morning by caesarean section.

I laughed. I laughed because one way or another, I was destined to have a repeat caesarean section. The Goddess of the Moon was dancing and now, I finally chose to dance with her.

I surrendered. There was no choice. There was nothing to fight any longer. The Universe had my back. Love not fear.

And there it was. I finally accepted my reality. There would be no homebirth. There would be no spiritual experience in the shower as I attempted to birth my baby all on my own. There would be none of that.

But what there was, was far more profound in many ways, because I was being asked to step beyond the fear and my idea of how things should be, and to experience the spiritual in all of this. This was the lesson that I had needed to learn, and this brought with it the spiritual experience and opportunity for growth that I had always dreamt of. It was just presenting itself in a way that I had not expected… but that's the way of the Universe. Our dreams always come true, but not as we expect them to; that too, is a lesson in surrender and acceptance.

CHAPTER 30

The Light of Surrender

Our lives were filled with light that Thursday morning, as if the surrendering brought with it a rush of support from the Universe.

There were Earth angels everywhere, as I was assigned the most beautifully funny and reassuring midwife, who was the embodiment of compassion and understanding. She was supported by another midwife, who happens to be the best friend of my cousin-in-law. It was perfect. Ladies who cared and who were in part familiar to me.

My parents kindly rushed around collecting some things for me from the cottage and dropping them into the ward, as we hadn't brought anything with us that morning. While I was deemed an emergency, we had some time, and all I asked was the opportunity to take a shower, which was granted.

I enjoyed standing bent over in the shower cubicle, the water washing over my back and cleansing me. I needed to feel clean ahead of the surgery. It also gave me time and space to be on my own too, processing events and coming to terms with my present reality. The last time I'd been in the exact same shower had been after Elijah's birth and I couldn't help thinking about the journey I'd been on since then.

The contracting had eased at that point, and I was feeling decidedly calm about everything. After some time, I dried myself and sat quietly, holding my precious lump of rose quartz, dropping awareness within and noticing how it felt, looking for any residual fear to let go of before the surgery. I then sat with my breath until I felt aligned and centred. I checked my pendulum, yes, now I was ready.

While I was showering, E was shown around the Neo-Natal Intensive Care Unit ("NICU") for babies, which I'd been shown around when I had been in hospital a few days earlier. I hadn't been too interested, because back then, I hadn't expected the baby to arrive at 34 weeks. Even now, I wasn't too fazed; there was mention that the baby may need support in the delivery room, but my sole focus was on the birth.

Back at my bed, the final arrangements were put in place. I had asked to keep my placenta and a tub was found for this. I'd also asked for vaginal seeding to take place, although this was refused me – the specialist almost laughed that I'd suggested it in the first place.

One of the reasons I had resisted a caesarean birth was due to the increased risk of health conditions in childhood, as the baby is deprived of the microbes that live in the mother's vagina.

One way around this is vaginal seeding, which involves collecting the mother's vaginal fluid on a piece of gauze prior to the birth and wiping this gauze over the baby's mouth, face and body directly after birth. This kick-starts the baby's immune system and gut by exposing the baby to a diverse mix of beneficial microbes.

However, I was told that this would be extremely risky, given that I had an infection, and the baby was being born so early. I accepted this easily, as the baby's wellbeing was paramount and I had to respect the knowledge and experience of the medical team, even if this went against my own understanding of things.

Birth

By late morning, they were ready for me in theatre and I was ready to meet my baby. I walked to theatre this time, which made a huge difference psychologically, as if I was giving my full consent to the process and not being pushed in a bed, as had happened previously.

Arriving at the theatre, it was still a relatively alien environment to me, although this time, I had none of the fear that had gripped me previously. The theatre nurse assigned to me was another Earth angel, who did all he could to care for me.

I knew with certainty that the Universe had my back and that I was being truly supported. I also had my mantra running constantly through my mind, "love not fear", and it was this that I repeated to myself as the spinal block was applied.

It was actually a relief to be anaesthetised because the contractions had started up again and it was challenging staying present to them and doing what was asked of me in terms of my positioning on the bed. The theatre nurses were very kind and I held one of their hands as I focused in on my breath.

The spinal block soon took effect and we went through the usual checks. I had made the anaesthetist aware of the issues I had experienced with Elijah's birth and she was another angel who kept talking to me and making sure that I felt OK. Before I knew it, E was beside me, wearing his blue theatre attire.

It all seemed to happen very quickly after that, and we held hands as our son was born at 12.21p.m. on Thursday 20th October 2016, with E watching over the screen. There he was, safely Earth-side, our little grounded warrior, Eben Ron McInnes, whose name had chosen itself months earlier.

We liked the name when we were looking at names for Elijah and we just had a sense that if we had another boy, he would be called Eben. The name is Hebrew and means "stone of help", and this felt rather appropriate to me because, in-utero, he felt grounded. Furthermore, I had this sense that this was a healing baby and would help in the world as he was now helping me.

As we had named Elijah after E's dad, Iain, we had agreed that if we had a boy, we would name him after my dad, Ron. The name comes from Old Norse and means "warrior", and he seemed to be living up to this name already.

Eben weighed 5 lb 1 oz, which was a brilliant weight for a baby born six weeks premature, but he needed oxygen upon delivery, and while I got a glance of him, he was immediately whisked away to the NICU, while I was stitched up again.

I was jubilant, we had another son, a gift from above. And his birth, too, was a gift, for I had been given the opportunity to embody surrender. This was all I had ever wanted to experience, the surrender that accompanies the birthing process. I, too, felt re-birthed.

There was nothing to fight against. There was just this incredible sense of peace and calmness. The Universe had our back. We were bathed in love, and with that came the realisation that this is all there is. We are all heart, just like my babies had shown me at their six-week scans. There is nothing to fear and nowhere else to be but in the moment.

We were in the flow, and that meant constantly surrendering to the present, whatever it may give. And I was grateful for this realisation over the coming week ahead.

CHAPTER 31

Love Not Fear

A few months prior to Eben's birth, I'd taught a charity yoga "*class on the grass*" to raise money for the Priaulx Premature Baby Foundation here in Guernsey. It was the second time I had raised money for this charity, and it seemed appropriate to do so whilst pregnant.

It's said that we create our own reality, and perhaps that was what I was doing, or perhaps on some level, I already knew. Who knows, but there is certainly a lot to be said for the law of attraction, what we attract into our life and the lessons we learn from this.

Furthermore, there's also the balance of giving and receiving, and it made me laugh that here now, I was receiving a box of goodies from the Foundation, where only months earlier, I'd been giving to them instead. It was a beautiful touch, which warmed my spirit as I visited Eben in the NICU for the first time.

I'd not really considered that my baby would be premature, nor that he would be separated from me at birth. I hadn't given it too much thought and no one had really mentioned it, as the primary focus had been about the birth.

There were many lessons I learned during this whole experience, not least that what we resist persists. Here I'd been, resisting a caesarean birth and yet, that had persisted. On some level, I needed to know that it could be a gentle, empowering, joyful, enlightening and healing experience. And I needed an opportunity to surrender.

I'd invited the Goddess of the Moon into my life and I'd danced with her. It was inevitable, therefore, that at some point, I would be cracked open. It is only in the cracking open that we let go of the encasing that holds our limited understanding of how things should be – and in so doing, allow the light to come in.

The light was certainly shining brightly in my life those next few days. I was high on the birth and held safely in my baby bubble of love. There was nothing to fear, all was well, the Universe had my back, and I was happy to flow with it.

This put me in good stead for the NICU, as I reminded myself of the need to continue to surrender to the unfolding of the present moment. "Love not fear" was still my mantra and I repeated this as often as I could, and kept my lump of rose quartz crystal close to me.

I was wheeled into the NICU on my bed straight from theatre, as I hadn't yet seen Eben properly and was keen to do so. I was able to hold him skin to skin, my teeny, tiny baby, who did a good job of trying to latch on to my nipple. In my naivety, I presumed that that was it, we would establish breastfeeding and he would come home with me.

EARLY DAYS

Unfortunately, this wasn't the case, and I believe it's one of those things that unless you have been through it yourself, you'll never truly know how it feels. Returning home from hospital without a baby is not ideal. Nor is having to set your alarm in the middle of the night to express milk for the baby, who is being cared for by someone else in the hospital, while you're at home alone with a deflating tummy.

The fact he had to take antibiotics tested me too. There he was, born into a sterile environment, and now taking medication that would kill any of the good bacteria he'd been born with. It didn't help that in those first few days, he was put on oxygen, which meant that I had very limited physical contact with him, and even then, my hands had to be washed repeatedly.

Within a week, my life had changed significantly, and it felt a little like the rug had been pulled from beneath my feet. Instead of going to the office every day, now, here I was, in the hospital, caring as best I could for my premature baby and trying to heal from a caesarean section.

I was also trying to make myself available to Elijah too, who was challenged by Mummy's sudden disappearance from his life. E would bring him to the hospital but he didn't understand what was going on and he couldn't appreciate that the baby would one day be coming home with us. This was perhaps the toughest bit at times, feeling torn between my boys.

The days in the windowless NICU were long, and I took time out at lunchtime to lie on my yoga mat in the small and empty visitor's room and feel the ground beneath me, dropping awareness into my breath, while channelling Reiki onto my scar. I chanted the Bija mantra too and was amazed at the powerful manner in which this brightened each of my chakras. I highly recommend all post-natal ladies chant the Bija mantra daily if they can.

I felt the need to move my body too, and practiced gently and intuitively, honouring the need to heal from the inside out. I made a point of lying on the floor with my legs raised on a bed, to help heal my womb. I also relaxed to free Yoga Nidra transcripts from the Yoga Nidra Network, which helped to integrate all layers of my being again.

My recovery from the caesarean section was quicker this time. I wasn't anaemic, which made a huge difference. Furthermore, there was nothing to fight against. The birth had been gentle and exactly what it needed to be, given the circumstances, and this brought with it a sense of peace. My faith had been truly restored and I felt deeply connected and aligned to the Goddess of the Moon and Source.

I also recognised that this was Eben's journey too. I believe that babies choose the manner in which they are born, for they have their own mission on Mother Earth. Eben Ron had chosen his name too, and here he was, embodying it. He certainly was a grounded warrior, his feet firmly on the ground and doing what was asked of him in the NICU, charming us all in the process.

In those first few days, both my mum and I channelled Reiki onto his chest at any available opportunity, and he was soon breathing without the need for oxygen. He responded well to the Reiki and I wish all premature babies had access to this energy to assist in their healing process.

After seven days, he was taken off the antibiotics too and then it was just a case of putting on weight and establishing breastfeeding. I was doing all I could to facilitate this, as I was desperate to strengthen his immune system through my breast milk, and I was keen that the nasal tube was removed.

I shall be forever indebted to angel nurse Eileen and to the Universe for sending her into our lives during this tricky time. She is a remarkable lady who really helped to keep my spirits high and brought so much love and laughter into the NICU. Our family and friends filled our lives with love and support too, and amazingly, Eben was home within two weeks; we felt truly blessed.

Bringing my baby home

Needless to say, it soon transpired that Eben has gut issues and a myriad of insensitivities, which I'm sure are a result of the manner in which he was birthed. There was no choice in this at the time, nor in his after-birth care, and I recognise that this is a part of our journey. It has opened up a whole new world to us, as we seek to heal his gut and strengthen his immune system.

It makes me laugh that even this has manifested – what we resist persists. I didn't want a caesarean section for this very reason, as it can often lead to gut issues for mother and baby, and I did all I could to try to prevent this, but it happened regardless. It is only now that I realise there was nothing to fear, that in bringing the shadows to light, we awake to the greater potential in life.

My dream had finally come true, just not in the way that I imagined. However, in the process, I had learned to dance with the Goddess of the Moon and had healed from my previous birthing experience. Furthermore, I've learned lessons in surrender, acceptance and trust, and I feel brighter as a result.

"Love not fear" shall always be my mantra, and I am eternally grateful to my boys for all they have taught me, both in-utero and in this world. They will always be my greatest spiritual teachers, as they constantly bring me back to the present and to the heart.

My journey to motherhood has been a gift in so many ways. I have embodied the spirit of new life, my heart has opened to greater love, and there has been a recognition that this is all there is. The Universe knows only love; it is we humans who create the rest. We are all heart, living in a world of love, and the sooner we all know and feel this, the better for humankind and Mother Earth.

I hope you enjoyed this book.
I would be delighted if you could
leave a review on Amazon.
Many thanks,
Emma Després

Acknowledgments

With a huge thank you, lots of love and gratitude to my amazing mum, Jill, for reading and checking every single one of my blog posts that led to this book - you're great! A huge thank you and much gratitude also to Katie Bisson for kindly putting the blog posts into some semblance of order and kindly checking for typos - and to Steph Bisson for working her magic with the website. A huge thank you and gratitude to Leila Green for her compassionate editorial skills and patience.

To E for putting up with me during the editorial process especially, but also for putting up with me generally and being everything I ever wished for in a soul mate and daddy, and more. To my boys, Elijah and Eben, for the play-time they missed with Mummy, while I busily tapped away each morning over breakfast, and throughout the first few months of Eben's life with him often attached to my breast! Thank you to my dad, Ron, just because he's my dad and because he raises my spirits when I'm struggling. Thank you also to my brother, Ross, who might live the other side of the world, but who is always there for me. A huge thank you of course to Mr Nzewi (what an amazing person you are) and the team at the Medical Specialist Group in Guernsey for all their care and support.

A huge, huge heartfelt thank you to the team at Wessex Fertility Clinic, especially Dr Sue Ingamells and Jo Payne without whom none of this would have ever been possible - it's amazing what you do! A big thank you also to my soul friend and doula, Anita Davies, we're lucky to have you on Guernsey. Also to the specialists who delivered Elijah and Eben, and to the many midwives, especially Alex and Flo, who helped during pregnancy and birth. Also a huge heartfelt thank you to Eileen Blake who helped to keep me sane during NICU, you'll never realise what a difference you made, you are always our angel. Thank you also to our special friends, for all your encouragement and support, you know who you are, we love you! Thank you to Jo de Diepold Braham for her integrity and healing work, and to Christine Shepherd, my soul moon friend, and fellow sea swimmer. And lastly but by no means least, to my students, who have been there throughout, thank you.

Printed in Great Britain
by Amazon